A Guide to
The Seashore

Ray Ingle

illustrated by Patricia Mynott

Hamlyn
London · New York · Sydney · Toronto

FOREWORD

'Oh, what an endless worke have I in hand,
To count the Sea's abundant progeny'

SPENSER

Although books on shore natural history are plentiful most of them
fall into one of three categories. The first deals with the biology,
behaviour and habitats of shore animals and plants; the second
gives information for identifying them, and a third, usually a
students' text-book, supplies details on their anatomy and external
structure.

This small volume attempts to combine all three categories and
is presented as a synopsis of sea-shore natural history. Because of
its modest price and size it has been necessary to impose a limitation
on the number of illustrations and the amount of text. Nevertheless,
it is hoped that it gives an overall impression of shore natural
history with emphasis on the predominant and more common animal
species – the invertebrates and primitive chordates – that occur on
the British and North European coasts.

Wherever possible actual specimens have been used as subjects
for the illustrations but it has been necessary also to draw upon
many of the standard works of reference. Full acknowledgement
is therefore given to the following sources: Gosse, E. 1896, *Naturalist
of the Sea Shore*, Heinemann (for figure 1). Hardy, A. 1958, *The
Open Sea*, Vol. 1. Collins (parts of figure 64). Buchsbaum, R. 1953,
Animals without Backbones, 2 vols. Penguin Books (for figures 65,
66, 71, 72, 78, 79, 82, 89, 95–99, 113, 114, 163, 220, 224, 228).
Bullough, W. S. 1960 *Practical Invertebrate Anatomy*, Macmillan Co.
(for figures 85–88). Fretter, V. & Graham, A. 1962, *British Prosobranch Molluscs*, Ray Society London. Bernard Quaritch (for figures
166–170).

R. I.

Published by The Hamlyn Publishing Group Limited
London · New York · Sydney · Toronto
Astronaut House, Feltham, Middlesex, England

Copyright © The Hamlyn Publishing Group Limited 1969
Reprinted 1972, 1973, 1975, 1,977
ISBN 0 600 00083 4

Phototypeset by BAS Printers Limited, Wallop, Hampshire
Colour separations by Schwitter Limited, Zurich
Printed in Spain by Mateu Cromo, Madrid

CONTENTS

Marine Biology

The sea-shore, with its numerous rock-pools exposed at low tide and usually covered with vast areas of seaweed, often arouses in us the desire to explore. A great deal of the coastline has been altered by Man's encroachment and the flora and fauna destroyed by effluents poured into the sea, however, it is still possible to find the seclusion and privacy that must have been enjoyed by those naturalists who pioneered sea-shore biology in the previous century.

The organized study of shore natural history can be said to date from that period of the eighteenth century when the Swedish botanist Carl Linnaeus published a practical classification of plants and animals. Although his original system has been greatly improved since, the basic principles of naming organisms as conceived by Linnaeus is still in use (page 154).

The building of the railways enabled the less prosperous Victorian families to take their holidays by the sea and it was during that century that the foundations of shore biology were established. The writings and illustrations by such Victorian naturalists as Philip Gosse, G. B. Sowerby and Charles Kingsley did much to inspire and guide both young and old in their explorations of the sea-shore. Philip Gosse appears to have been the first person to actually hold classes on the shore for . . . 'Those who desire to make themselves acquainted with the living objects which the shore produced.' Edmund Gosse, his son, recalled the following account of his father's shore explorations with these words. 'I recall a long desultory line of persons on a beach of shells – doubtless at Barricome. At the head of the procession, like Apollo conducting the Muses, my father strides ahead in an immense wide-awake loose black coat and trousers, and fisherman's boots, with a collecting basket in one hand, a staff or prod in the other. Then follow gentlemen of every age, all seeming spectacled and old to me, and many ladies in the balloon costume of 1855, with shawls falling in a point from between their shoulders to the edge of their flounced petticoats, each wearing a mushroom hat with streamers.'

1 Philip Gosse

2 Anton Dohrn

3 Stazione Zoologica, Naples

3

4

4 The Plymouth Marine Laboratory

Philip Gosse [1] was born in 1810, the son of a painter of miniatures. He was a successful writer on natural history but ill health compelled his retirement to Devonshire. Here, with his family, his recuperation stimulated him to produce some of the best Victorian writings on marine natural history. Three books, *A Naturalist's Rambles on the Devonshire Coast* (1853), *Tenby; A Sea-Side Holiday* (1856), and *A Year at the Shore* (1865), brought to him lasting fame and some financial reward. In addition to these delightful books on shore life he wrote many important scientific works. Of these he is perhaps best remembered for his *Natural History of Mollusca* (1854), *A Manual of Marine Zoology for the British Isles* (1855–56) and the beautifully illustrated *Actinologia Britannica; a History of the British Sea-Anemones and Corals* (1860). These contributions were the forerunners of the numerous books that followed in this century, a selection of which are listed from pages 154 to 157.

If Gosse was to bring the delights of the shore into the Victorian home, Anton Dohrn [2] was to pioneer the establishment of the first large scientific marine station. Dohrn was born at Stettin in 1840. He grew up sharing his father's interests in music, drama and entomology and although he had intentions of becoming a bookseller his outlook was changed when he read Charles Darwin's *The Origin of Species*. Dohrn became interested in animal development and felt the need for a laboratory near the coast where he could collect and study his growing organisms. After many difficulties he finally had the famous marine station built at Naples.

This Zoological Station (Stazione Zoologica) [3] is set near the coast in the beautiful public park, the Villa Nazionale in the suburb of Chiasia, Naples. It was completed in 1874 and after the First World War the Station became a trust. It is famed for the aquarium and research facilities provided for scientists of all nations and is today directed by the founder's grandson, Dr Peter Dohrn.

In Great Britain the Plymouth Marine Laboratory, owned by the Marine Biological Association of the United Kingdom, was opened in 1888. A small part of the funds for its upkeep is derived from the famous 'table system' in which members or societies pay annually towards the upkeep of a table or laboratory bench for research students. Much of the research done here is published in the Association's *Journal of the Marine Biological Association* that is issued quarterly.

5 An attempt to capture the mood of one of the renowned collecting expeditions on the Devonshire coast and lead by Gosse

5

The enthusiastic naturalists depicted in figure 5 would be represented today by a class of students and their lecturer participating in one of the numerous courses at a marine station. There are now many marine stations on the European coast that have replaced the former individual naturalists. Considerable numbers of scientists specialize in particular aspects of marine research, or work as teams on particular projects.

These projects, undertaken by the various research teams, may vary from a pure hydrological study of the inshore waters, to critical identifications of the local plants and animals inhabiting all stretches of the shore. The recent Parliamentary report on the *Torrey Canyon* disaster, for example, was produced by the combined efforts of the many marine biologists studying the effects of oil pollution on the shore and off-shore animals and plants.

Many of these marine stations are administered by universities or similar bodies and some specialize in certain aspects of marine science, such as fishery biology. In the Mediterranean the most renowned is the Stazione Zoologica and a conspicuous coastal feature of the Principality of Monaco is the imposing marine laboratory, founded by Prince Albert I and now directed by Captain J. Y. Costeau.

The small laboratory at Banyuls-sur-Mer, on the French Mediterranean coast, and the one at Concarneau, figure 6, (33) also provide research facilities for visiting scientists, as does the famous Plymouth Laboratory (21). The Stations at Port Erin (26), Cullercoats (17), Menai Bridge (24) and Whitstable (20) are visited throughout the year by students and scientists while knowledge of the flora and fauna of the Clyde Estuary has been enhanced by studies made at the Millport Laboratory (27) founded in 1897. Although the fjords of the Norwegian coasts do not provide the same expanse of beach and foreshore as those farther south, nevertheless valuable information has been collected on deep water animals by workers at the Trondheim (3) and Helsingor (10) laboratories.

The new Bergen marine station, to quote but one example, was opened in 1957 and has a well-designed building and very excellent laboratory facilities. The laboratory also has a research vessel that is well equipped for dredging in the deep fjords, which sometimes reach depths of 1,200 metres.

There are now over 500 marine stations scattered throughout the world, as far apart as the famous Woods Hole Marine Biological Laboratory, near Cape Cod, Massachusetts in the United States, to the Seto Marine Laboratory in Japan.

6 Location of some marine stations of the North European coast

1 Reykjavic	10 Helsinor	19 Burnham	28 Heligoland
2 Faeroes	11 Charlottenlund	20 Whitstable	29 Bremerhaven
3 Trondheim	12 Kiel	21 Plymouth	30 Den Helder
4 Bergen	13 Gdynia	22 Haverfordwest	31 Ijmuiden
5 Oslo	14 Aberdeen	23 Cork	32 Roscoff
6 Helsinki	15 St Andrews	24 Menai Bridge	33 Concarneau
7 Årendal	16 Edinburgh	25 Conway	34 Arachon
8 Lysekil	17 Cullercoats	26 Port Erin	
9 Göteborg	18 Lowestoft	27 Millport	

Shaping of the Coastline

England and Wales have approximately 2,750 miles of coast washed by the sea. The overall shape of the coastline was originally determined by the deposition of rocks during the past history of the earth, but it is, however, always undergoing changes caused by waves and wind action. Sometimes these changes are very obvious, as might be seen after a violent storm, but generally changes of the coastline are almost imperceptible and take place gradually over a long period of time.

The waves causing these changes are produced by winds moving the surface of the water. The steady push of the wind causes the water to rise, fall and roll as is illustrated in figure 7. However, it is only in coastal waters that waves are effective in moving particles off the sea bottom and their full effect is very apparent when they break upon the shore.

Waves usually strike the shore at an oblique angle. The mass of water, known as the swash or send, is powerful enough to carry sand and shingle – sometimes large stones – up on to the beach. Some of the swash percolates downwards into the beach sand or shingle but the remainder, called the backwash, runs off the surface into the sea carrying beach material with it. Stones and sand are thus returned to the sea by the backwash of one wave and may be carried up on to the beach again by the swash of the succeeding wave. As this movement is an oblique one, the material composing the beach will be advanced along the

7 Wave formation

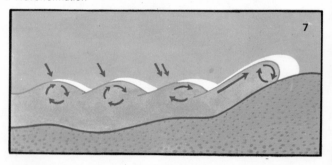

8 Mechanics of beach drift

shore by successive swash and backwash as each wave breaks. Figure 8 illustrates the movement of beach material diagrammatically as incoming waves migrate along the shore carrying material with them.

The direction of advance of the sand and shingle along a beach is very obvious on those beaches where breakwaters have been constructed to prevent excessive beach drifting. The sand and shingle will be piled higher on one side of the breakwater than on the other side as shown in figure 9. Breakwaters are often the first objects exposed by the ebbing tide and are well worth exploring for the countless forms of smaller sea-weeds and encrusting animals attached to their surfaces. There are often numerous crustaceans trapped in the small pools formed at the breakwater base by the outgoing tide.

9 Evidence of beach drift-breakwaters

Waves can be destructive or constructive in their effect upon the beach. Destructive waves tend to be large ones. They break vertically and their rapid backwash leaves little time for percolation of the water into the sand or shingle. In extreme cases such waves can undercut cliffs causing collapse of the upper parts. This falls on to the beach and is slowly broken up by further wave action, washed along the coast and deposited as finer particles on another part of the shore.

Constructive waves are smaller and break much more obliquely on the shore. They have an energetic swash with a much slower backwash so that a greater part of this water will percolate into the beach sand or shingle as the water runs back into the sea. These waves often deposit shingle, sand or mud in the off-shore region and, if the conditions are suitable, these deposits will build up into an off-shore bar.

Figure 10 shows, in a diagrammatic form, five types of beaches that are the indirect result of wave action. To the

left, in the foreground, is a rocky shore, which has rock pools and quantities of boulders and stones. The latter are the results of the erosion and undercutting of the cliffs by wave action. Farther along the coast is a shingle beach resulting from the breaking up and deposition of small particles of cliff rock. This shingle is further broken down into sand and deposited to form a sandy beach. This type of beach often forms a bay between two rocky headlands as illustrated.

The finest particles of material are deposited as mud, and this, along with the mud carried down by river water, forms a muddy shore. This latter type of shore is characteristic of estuaries. Finally, if an off-shore bar is formed parallel to the shore it may extend to join with the shore and cut off the sea completely thus giving rise to an enclosed lagoon as shown in the right of this figure. The water in a lagoon is usually diluted by rainwater and therefore is, for much of the time, far less saline than that of the adjacent sea.

10 This composite illustration shows the five types of beaches that can result from the combined effects of wind and waves shaping the coastline. On the left are cliffs that are being subjected to erosive action of the sea. The resulting deposition of rocks has given rise to the seaweed covered rockpools as shown in the mid-foreground. The further breaking up of the rock has produced a shingle beach and further along the coast, before and beyond the last headland prominence, is a sandy beach resulting from further erosive action. In the estuary are the sandy mud-flats, typical of this location. If conditions are right an off-shore bar can be formed that can give rise to a lagoon as shown on the right.

The deposition of beach material is termed accretion and this process often leads to important and marked changes in the shape of the coastline. The accretion of shingle, for example, has lead to the great forelands developed at Dungeness, in Kent and at Orfordness, in Suffolk.

Perhaps the most striking examples of beach accretion are to be seen in the development of the salt marshes. Here the deposits of mud and sand are laid down in the more sheltered regions of the coast, where the action of the tide is minimal. The plants that become first established in these regions are often seaweeds such as *Enteromorpha*. The fronds of these serve as traps for the further accretion of muddy sand and also allow other plants to appear as the beach deposits grow. Then such forms as Glasswort, Cord Grass and Eel Grass become established. All these are flowering plants and their roots provide suitable regions for further accretion.

On the higher parts of this now well-formed marsh other flowering plants will appear, such as Sea Lavender and Sea Aster. As the salinity decreases, due to the seaward extension of the marsh, forms such as Thrift will appear often followed by Sea Rush and eventually plants usually confined to inland regions will become established. It is then that freshwater pools will make their appearance. The development of these is often enhanced by the building of a sea wall and so the land, once fenced off, can be drained and used in time for agricultural purposes. However, before the land can be fully developed, sufficient time must elapse for the salt content of the soil to diminish so that grass, for cattle grazing and later arable crops, can become established. This process of reclamation can take many years.

The early establishment of plants on coastal accretions can result in the formation of sand dunes. Dunes are primarily the stabilization of wind-blown sand. Plants involved in dune production are such forms as Sea Couch Grass and Marram Grass. This latter plant can grow and spread very rapidly and has been instrumental in the establishment of many sand dune regions that later become colonized by other sand inhabiting plants such as Sand Fescue and Sea Holly. Dune heaths are well developed in regions of the British Isles such as Norfolk and Cornwall. In the latter region the sand, because of its rich calcium carbonate content, is used to provide calcium to the soil. In many regions these heaths provide excellent golf courses.

A shore with rock pools is usually the most popular collecting ground for the marine biologist. Sheltered rocky shores are usually rich in species of plants and animals, particularly when the rocks are thickly covered with weeds. These provide a suitable substrate for many encrusting animals, such as hydroids (page 58) and polyzoans (page 135), and protect many delicate forms against desiccation. Only a few animals have established themselves on exposed and wave-beaten rocky shores. The most frequently encountered of these are the crustacean barnacles (page 92) and a few molluscs such as *Patella* and *Mytilus* (pages 114 and 124).

Shingle beaches offer poor footholds for animals and plants, as the pebbles composing beaches are large so that the spaces between them cannot retain water. In addition, shingle is far more unstable than sand and animals and plants are easily crushed between the rolling pebbles.

Sandy beaches usually have a less pronounced slope than shingle beaches and, because of their smaller particle size, are much slower to drain when uncovered at low tide. Sand, with a high water content, affords easier passage to many animals that burrow into this medium and it is in sandy beaches that many of the burrowing animals live, concealed and protected from desiccation at low tide. Typical inhabitants of this medium are the polychaete worms (page 76) and many molluscs (page 110).

Muddy shores, with their almost imperceptible slope, are often typical of estuaries where they are termed mud flats. Mud contains much organic matter that forms the food for many burrowing forms, especially polychaetes. Mud is deposited where there is limited water movement and in this stable medium many animals are able to make fairly permanent burrows. There is often a gradation from sand to mud with a corresponding change in the types of inhabitants, although very few animals can live in pure mud. The estuaries of rivers and lagoons provide conditions ranging from low to high salinities with a corresponding gradation of plant and animal life.

The Tides

A conspicuous feature of much of the coastline is the periodic rise and fall of the tides. A connection between the retreat 'ebb' and the advance 'flow' of the tide and the phases of the moon was recognized many centuries before it was understood how the moon's gravitational pull could produce a tidal effect on the earth's surface-water directly connected with the phases of the moon.

Perhaps the most impressive feature about the tides is their almost monotonous regularity and their predictable variability. A high or low tide occurs on the coasts of the British Isles approximately every twelve hours twenty-five minutes. At least one period in every month the tide reaches its maximum flow and ebb. This occurs about two days after a full and a new moon and it is called a spring tide although it bears no relationship to the particular season of the year. Between the periods of spring tides there is a time when the ebb and flow of the water is at its minimum, this is the time of neap tide. In September and March, usually about the 21st, when the day is equal (equi) to night (nox) the tidal equinoxes occur. These are the periods of the highest and lowest spring tides of the year and it is only at these times that the shore biologist can collect from the lowest part of the exposed shore that is not normally accessible at other times.

The general direction of the two tidal waves that flow around the British Isles every twelve hours is shown in figure 11. The path of water, however, is influenced by very many complex factors and the rising and falling of the water at various points on the coast is affected by tidal currents and centrifugal forces as the earth spins. Great differences are often found when the tides at the different localities are compared and a study of the predicted times of high tide for January 7th 1967 for the regions shown on the map will soon reveal the complex nature of this tidal wave. The height of the tide also varies considerably, for example, the average height of the spring tide at London Bridge is about 20 feet while Avonmouth has a 40 foot rise and in contrast to this Portland has a mere 7 foot spring tide.

11 There are two tidal waves that flow around the British Isles every twelve hours and their paths are indicated by arrows on the above map. Various coastal stations are shown, together with tide predictions for 7 January 1967. The times are in Greenwich Mean Time.

1 Lands End, 13.48 hrs
2 Bournemouth, 7.19 hrs
3 Brighton, 8.04 hrs
4 Herne Bay, 8.58 hrs
5 Yarmouth, 5.41 hrs
6 Wells-on-Sea, 15.53 hrs
7 Hornsea, 14.02 hrs

8 Dunbar, 11.16 hrs
9 Aberdeen, 11.03 hrs
10 Thurso, 5.11 hrs
11 Oban, 14.55 hrs
12 Llandudno, 7.24 hrs
13 Cardiff, 15.59 hrs

When a tidal wave enters a river estuary or a shallow region of the coast its form becomes distorted. This often causes a rapid flow and a slower ebb and in extreme cases gives rise to a tidal bore or wall of water that will move rapidly up the estuary.

Influenced by the regular rhythm of the sun and moon, tidal movements can be predicted with a fair degree of accuracy, although the effects of wind, for example, can often affect the predicted height of the water. Such was the case in the storm surge of 1953 that caused havoc and destruction on the British and Dutch coasts. By combining astronomical and meteorological observations it is now usually possible to forecast these surges at least twelve hours ahead of their occurrence. In Great Britain an Official Flood Warning Service is now operated by the Meteorological Office and the Hydrographic Department of the Admiralty.

The energy produced during tidal movements is enormous. It has been estimated that the potential tidal energy of water entering the English Channel is in the region of 180,000 megawatts but the greater part of this energy is dissipated by friction. It is not surprising therefore that many schemes have been devised to harness this power of the tides. The only one in operation at the present time is the tidal generating station in the estuary of the River Rance, near St. Malo, Brittany. The water can only flow in and out of this estuary through tunnels in a large dam blocking the

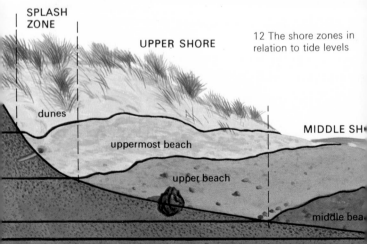

SPLASH ZONE

UPPER SHORE

12 The shore zones in relation to tide levels

dunes

MIDDLE SH

uppermost beach

upper beach

middle bea

river mouth. Its passage through each tunnel is made to drive the propellers of a turbo-alternator that can give an output of about ten megawatts of electricity.

The average high and low tide levels occur between the spring and neap tides. Thus, the part of the shore that is most frequently covered by the average high tide, abbreviated A H T L, and exposed at the average low tide level, A L T L, is the middle shore [12]. The lower shore is only uncovered at low spring tides and the upper shore covered only at high spring tides. Above the upper shore is the splash zone, so called because it receives the spray of the high spring tides. These divisions of the shore tend to correspond to the differences in shore populations of animals and plants.

The unceasing regularity of the covering and uncovering by the tide of shore-dwelling animals has imposed upon them a rhythmic behaviour pattern. This becomes apparent when animals are removed from their natural habitat on the shore and kept in captivity such as in an aquarium. For example, the little flatworms called *Convoluta roscoffensis* come to the surface of the sand, in which they live, in great numbers when covered by the tide. Conversely at low tide they descend into the sand as it dries. When these flatworms are placed in an aquarium and vertical glass tubes are substituted for their burrows, they perform this upward and downward migration that coincides approximately with the flow and ebb of the shore tide. This endogenous rhythm as it is called, can last for eight days. Similar rhythms are known to occur in the Ragworm, *Nereis diversicolor* (page 76) and in the Rough Periwinkle, *Littorina saxalis* (page 116). The latter species normally inhabits the upper shore and when kept in captivity shows activity once every fifteen days that coincide with the period of spring tides.

12

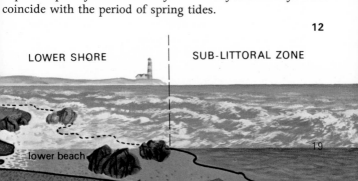

LOWER SHORE   SUB-LITTORAL ZONE

lower beach

Names and Arrangement of Animals and Plants

The 'Harbour Crab', the 'Joe Rocker Crab', 'Green Crab', the 'Shore Crab' and the 'Common Shore Crab' are all names that aptly describe the many features about this crustacean, but these common or vernacular names can give rise to confusion about the exact identity of the animal in question. At times such names can even mislead. For example, the 'Dublin Bay Prawn' is not a prawn but a Lobster and is also found off parts of the European coast other than in Dublin Bay. Marine biologists therefore prefer to call the shore or green crab by the title of *Carcinus maenas*. The practice of giving each animal and plant two names follows the established system that was introduced by the Swedish naturalist Carl Linnaeus. It is known as a binomial system (two names) of nomenclature and dates from 1758, when the tenth edition of Linnaeus' *Systema Naturae* was published, from which date the science of taxonomy can be said to have begun. This double name is accepted by scientists throughout the world and it leaves no doubt as to which species is being discussed.

Some scientific names aptly describe the animal or plant to which they are applied, for example *Macropodia* 'long footed', *longirostris* 'long rostrum' crab. Some are very similar but apply in fact to totally unrelated groups such as *Alcyonidium* (Phylum Polyzoa) and *Alcyonium* (Phylum Cnidaria). Despite these minor shortcomings it is preferable to use the scientific name rather than the vernacular one. In reference 54 some of the regulations governing their application are discussed in more detail. It is sufficient to mention here that the practice adopted in this book is to use the scientific name followed by the vernacular one (page 154). Many plants and animals do not have common names.

Much of life is taken up with subconsciously classifying many of the objects that surround us and this is important and necessary to progress in an orderly manner. The plants and animals in this book are therefore arranged according to accepted schemes of classification that are used by biologists. It is necessary to consult references 7, 54 and 55 for details of these classifications, as space does not permit their inclusion in this book.

Plants of the Seashore

The plant life of the shore, below the splash zone, is chiefly represented by the diverse forms of algae ranging from microscopic unicellular diatoms and desmids to the larger multicellular seaweeds. In the splash zone region may be seen species of lichens, forming variably coloured encrusting growths on rocks.

A few flowering plants have established themselves on the shore such as Eel Grass, Glasswort and Sea Purslane, all characteristically inhabitants of salt marshes. The most dominant plants of the shore, at low tide, are undoubtedly the seaweeds. Some of these cover the exposed rocks, concealing and preventing the drying out of the many delicate shore animals. Others, including some of the more fragile forms, are to be found in rock pools and often provide a substrate for the many colonial invertebrates as well as furnishing food for other animals.

There are some 800 species of seaweeds occurring in the waters of the British Isles, many of the common species can be identified with the aid of a hand lens or by normal inspection. 'Sea-weeding' was a much favoured pastime of the Victorians and seaweed albums and prints were very fashionable. That era saw the publication of many popular and instructive books on seaweeds such as Gifford's (1848) *The Marine Botanist*, Landsborough's (1849) *A Popular History of British Seaweeds* and Clarke's (1865) *Common Seaweeds of the British Coast*. The enthusiasm for collecting these plants must have been enhanced by the appearance of the beautifully illustrated volumes of Professor William Henry Harvey's *Phycologia Brittanica* (1846–51) and Johnson and Croall's *Nature Printed British Seaweeds* (1859–60). Both are now collectors' pieces.

Seaweeds have been used by Man for many purposes, although their full potential use on a large scale has never been exploited. Communities that have recognized the value of seaweeds as an additive to enrich the soil are coastal farmers and, in Great Britain, farmers on the west coast in particular have consistently collected Oarweeds and Wracks that have been either ploughed into the soil or made into a compost for later use. The additional salt thus added to the soil seems to favour good growth of crop plants such as cabbage, swedes and mangolds. Seaweeds for manuring purposes are now sold commercially as a dried powdered fertilizer that is often used for dressing clover and grass. It is chiefly the nitrogen and potassium compounds derived from these weeds that enrich the soil, but some species, especially coralline weeds, also add lime to the soil.

In the eighteenth century an industry known as the 'kelp industry' was a flourishing concern in Great Britain. Kelp is the name given to the ash resulting from burned seaweed, chiefly Wracks, and this ash provided the necessary supplies of soda and salt used in the manufacture of glass and soap. The kelp industry originated in France but by 1720 it appears to have been well established in Ireland and Scotland. Before the discovery of kelp, soda and salt were extract d from a burnt succulent marsh plant called Glasswort (*Salicornia*). The ash from this was called 'barilla'. At times barilla became scarce, particularly during the American war of Independence (1775–81) and during the Peninsula War (1807–14), and at these times the price of kelp rose considerably. The kelp industry reached its peak of financial success when it was discovered that iodine could be extracted from Oarweeds (*Laminaria*). A decline in the financial prosperity of the industry began when large deposits of saltpetre were discovered in Chile, from which iodine could be produced at a much cheaper price than from processing seaweeds. The final blow came when large deposits of common salt were found at Stassfurt in Germany that was to provide a very cheap supply of this chemical.

An important derivative from seaweeds, especially the Oarweeds (*Laminaria*), is a substance known as alginic acid. This acid was first discovered by E. C. Stanford in 1883 but it was not until 1934, or thereabouts, that the alginate industry began with the marketing of a transparent wrapping paper that had been made from alginate derivatives. Today many forms of alginates are available that have wide applications. Sodium alginate, for example, is used in many food preparations. It is a stabilizing medium for ice-cream and a thickening agent in sauces and soups.

22

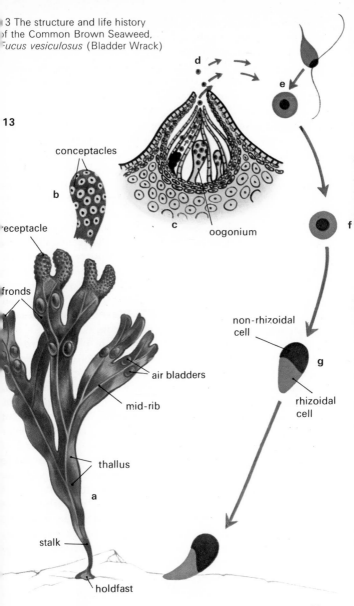

3 The structure and life history of the Common Brown Seaweed, *Fucus vesiculosus* (Bladder Wrack)

13

conceptacles

b

c

oogonium

receptacle

fronds

air bladders

mid-rib

thallus

a

stalk

holdfast

d

e

f

non-rhizoidal cell

g

rhizoidal cell

Another well-known seaweed produce is agar. This is chiefly extracted from tropical redweeds but during World War II Far Eastern supplies of agar became very scarce and it was necessary to extract this chemical from our local seaweeds. *Chondrus crispus* (page 38) and *Gigartina stellata* (page 36) were found suitable for this purpose. Agar is used as an emulsifier, an additive to canned meat and fish and a culture medium in bacteriology. Another substance called 'carragheen', extracted from the Red weed, *Chondrus crispus*, is employed in industry for stabilizing chocolate and is still used by Hebridean housewives for 'gelling' milk jellies.

A few seaweeds are consumed by animals and Man. The Red or Edible Dulse, *Rhodymenia palmata* (page 38), is eaten by cattle in North Brittany and is also served as an appetizer in parts of Scotland, while the Wrack *Fucus vesiculosus* (page 32) is grazed by pigs in Scotland and is called Pigweed. On parts of the Scottish coast sheep and horses may be seen grazing the Channelled Wrack, *Pelvetia canaliculata* (page 35). In South Wales and Ireland the gelatinous red *Porphyra* (page 36) is boiled to produce 'Laver Bread', a brownish jelly rich in vitamins B and C. The laver bread is usually coated with oatmeal and fried with bacon.

Seaweeds belong to the sub-kingdom of plants called the Thallophyta although the term 'algae' is often applied to them and related forms (diatoms). The thallophytes do not produce flowers or embryos and are without true roots, stems or leaves. Figure 13 shows the typical structure and life history of a common Brown Seaweed, *Fucus vesiculosus* (Bladder Wrack). The plant [a] is a mere flattened cellular expansion, the thallus, that grades into a stalk attached firmly to a rock surface by a holdfast. The cells composing the thallus are in tightly packed rows with thick jelly-like cell walls that afford protection and give flexibility against the pounding waves. Each thallus has a mid-rib and on either side of this, at intervals, are located the small air-bladders, rapidly formed in the spring by the growing plant. These bladders increase its buoyancy and bring the terminal parts of the plant nearer the surface of the water and to the light when covered by the tide. The end of the thallus is divided into fronds some of which are swollen and termed receptacles. In the spring the surface of each receptacle [b] is covered with small protruding dots, the conceptacles; each has a minute opening. The conceptacle [d] is a small cup and attached to its internal wall are pear-shaped oogonia. Each oogonium produces eight egg cells (ova) as shown for the female plant illustrated. The walls of the oogonium break and release the ova. These are extruded in minute drops of jelly on to the surface of the conceptacle. A similar process occurs in the male plant but here sperm cells (spermatozoids) are produced and these are very motile. A male spermatozoid unites with a female egg cell (fertilization) [e] after which the egg cell is called a zygote. [f]. This floats in the sea and divides into two cells that form the pear-shaped rhizoid [g]. Cell division continues and the upper cells, the non-rhizoid cells, will give rise to the thallus part of the plant whilst the lower rhizoid cells form the stalk and holdfast. This will occur after the rhizoid has settled on to a rock surface [h].

An individual plant produces millions of egg cells during the reproductive season but only a small proportion of these will germinate. Many are eaten by marine animals and others fail to settle in places suitable for growing. Many of the fronds without conceptacles are responsible for the vegetative reproduction of the plant for these simply grow and divide to increase the dimensions of the individual plants. Some however will develop receptacles to take part in the following year's reproductive cycle.

Seaweeds also reproduce by spore formation. This is a non-sexual (vegetative) process. These spores are manufactured in organs called sporangia. In some species, such as *Asperococcus fistulosus* [22] these are conspicuous on the surface of the fronds during the reproductive season. Each spore can give rise to a new plant.

There are many factors influencing the settlement and growth of seaweeds. Unlike land plants their environment is affected greatly by the rhythms of the rising and falling tides and this is related to the ability of many species to withstand exposures for long or short periods as, for example, between spring and neap tides. This factor will determine the position of a species on the shore as is well demonstrated by the zonation of the Wracks (page 32). Secure footholds for the settlement of the rhizoid stage is important and thus moving shingle beaches are usually devoid of seaweeds. Temperature of the water also affects the distribution of many species. The warm-water Mediterranean species, *Padina pavonia* make only a brief appearance each summer in selected habitats on the Dorset–Cornish coast, while some northern forms are totally absent from the southern coasts of England. The degree of exposure to wave action can also influence distribution and shape of seaweeds. *Ascophyllum nodosum*, Knotted Wrack [34] for example, is usually abundant in sheltered bays and may be scarce or absent on exposed shores. In localities greatly affected by wave action the surviving plants of *Fucus vesiculosus*, Bladder Wrack [31], have narrow fronds that are devoid of air bladders.

Seaweeds are classified into three phyla, the green sea-

14 *Enteromorpha intestinalis*   15 *Ulva lactuca*, Sea Lettuce

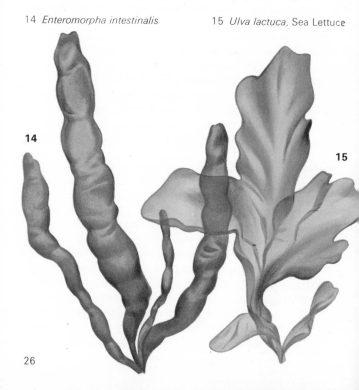

14

15

weeds (Phylum Chlorophyta), the brown seaweeds (Phylum Phaeophyta), and the red seaweeds (Phylum Rhodophyta). Colour, however, is not always a reliable guide as some reds have a brownish tint and many browns are an olive green. Most seaweeds will lose their colours when preserved.

The exact identification of some species is a task for an expert but the illustrations on the following pages should assist the beginner in identifying many of the more common species. Reference 7 should be consulted for more detailed identifications.

Green Seaweeds (Phylum Chlorophyta)

Ulva lactuca, Sea Lettuce, has delicate-looking fronds that may grow to over 12 inches in length and nearly as broad. The reproductive bodies appear throughout the year, first along the thallus margin and then spread over the surface and male and female reproductive bodies occur on separate plants. Sea Lettuce will thrive in sheltered bays especially where the water is slightly polluted. It has a world-wide distribution and is sold in the markets of Canton and Pekin as food and medicine. The elongated and tubular fronds of *Enteromorpha intestinalis* and two other species of this genus, *E. compressa* and *E. linza*, are one cell thick and the fronds can reach 24 inches in length. This species is very common and often abundant in shore pools that have been diluted with rain water. In sheltered pools it can reach a very large size with fronds up to 3 inches in width.

Enteromorpha linza [16] has flattened fronds that grow to 9 inches long and distinguish it from the former species. It is widely distributed and often found in sub-littoral waters and sometimes in brackish pools. *Bryopsis plumosa* [18] is widely distributed in the south of England and this species, 4 inches long, grows on the sides of deep pools or beneath ledges, on the middle shore. *Cladophora rupestris* [17] is a common moss-like plant growing to 5 inches long on the walls of mid-shore pools during the summer. It is often found beneath the Bladder Wrack. *Codium tomentosum* [19] and *Codium fragile* are very difficult to tell apart. The former species grows to 12 inches and provides food for many marine animals particularly the Sea Slug *Hermaea dendritica*.

27

16 *Enteromorpha linza*
17 *Cladophora rupestris*
18 *Bryopsis plumosa*
19 *Codium tomentosum*

Brown Seaweeds (Phylum Phaeophyta)

Chordaria flagelliformis is a slimy plant with the thin fronds growing up to 2 feet in length although 9 inches is the average length. Occurring in mid-shore pools and on rocks it is widely distributed and common during the summer months. *Leathesia difformis*, a very common species often growing on other seaweeds, is 2 inches in length and usually abundant in July.

The fronds of *Asperococcus fistulosus* [22] may reach 18 inches in length. During the reproductive phase the surface of the fronds are stippled with minute spore cells 'sporangia' each bearing minute filaments giving the plant a bristly appearance. It is a common species during the summer on the middle shore. *Ectocarpus siliculosus* is a very variable species with gelatinous fronds reaching 12 inches in length. It is reasonably abundant on the mid- and lower shore growing on rocks and on larger seaweeds. Its yellowish to pale green colour can distinguish it from *E. tomentosus*, a brownish olive green species. *Scytosiphon lomentaria* [24] has narrow tubular fronds that grow to 16 inches in length and are recognized by their characteristic

20 *Chordaria flagelliformis*
21 *Leathesia difformis*
22 *Asperococcus fistulosus*

23 *Ectocarpus siliculosus*
24 *Scytosiphon lomentaria*
25 *Chorda filum*

constrictions occurring every inch or so. It is a very common seaweed of the middle rocky shore and widely distributed in both northern and southern hemispheres.

Chorda filum [25] is often known as 'Dead Men's Ropes' or 'Mermaids' Tresses'. The slippery cord-like fronds of this species may grow to nearly 20 feet in length but have a uniform diameter of $\frac{1}{8}$ to $\frac{1}{4}$ of an inch, tapering at the extremity. During the early summer, in the reproductive period, the fronds are covered with spore cells. The long twisted tough masses of this weed have been known to entangle swimmers, whereby it gets its name. It is a very abundant plant during the summer months often in sheltered situations on the lower shore downwards to 10 fathoms, although it can sometimes be found in brackish water.

The family to which the following four species belong, the Laminariaceae, contain some of the largest known seaweeds that predominate in cold and temperate waters. They are represented on the British coast by the Oarweeds or

26 *Laminaria digitata*
27 *Laminaria hypeborea*, Cuvie

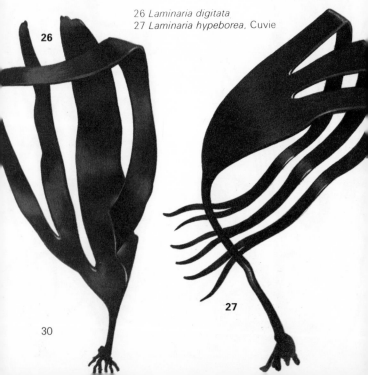

28 *Laminaria saccharina*, Sea Belt
29 *Saccorhiza polyschides*, Furbelows

Tangles. *Laminaria digitata* is called the Tangle. This weed [26] grows to 10 feet or more and its strap-like fronds, when mature, can measure 2 feet in width. The oldest fronds often support the Red weed, *Rhodymenia palmata* [48]. Tangle occupies the lower shore downwards into the littoral zone. In parts of Scandinavia the plant is boiled and added to meal of cattle food. *Laminaria hypeborea* [27], is the Cuvie. The lower half of the thallus region of this species is often covered with small pores that exude mucilage and provide a good surface for the attachment of many smaller seaweeds and this feature distinguishes it from the former species. Cuvie is confined to the littoral zone but at low tide its belt of brown fronds can harbour many of the smaller invertebrates. *Laminaria saccharina* [28] is known as Sea Belt or Poor Man's Weather Glass. This species is immediately recognized by its ribbon like fronds that can grow up to 5 feet in length. It occurs in sheltered coastal regions in deep pools and in the sub-littoral zone down to 10 fathoms. When dried the fronds are often coated with a white powder that is sweet to taste, a feature that has given it the name 'sugar wrack'. As the fronds tend to become limp with a

30 *Fucus serratus*, Toothed Wrack
31 *Fucus vesiculosus*, Bladder Wrack
32 *Fucus spiralis*, Spiral Wrack

rise in air humidity, and brittle as the air becomes dry, it is popularly used for weather forecasting. *Saccorhiza polyschides* [29] or Furbelows is a large plant growing to 15 feet and up to 12 feet in width. The species grows on the lower shore downwards and the plants inhabiting deeper waters are the largest. The thallus is typically expanded into a wavy frill and is often cast up on to the beach in large quantities.

The family to which the following five species belong, the Fucaceae represent the better known forms of Brown seaweeds called the Wracks. These species usually appear on the shore in defined zones. They do not produce spores and reproduce only by sexual and vegetative growth. The former importance of some of these brown seaweeds was in the ash (kelp) resulting from burning the weed. This kelp contained large amounts of soda and potash and was formally the chief source of soda used by the glass and soap industries. *Fucus serratus* is the Toothed or Serrated Wrack.

This species [30] has a poor tolerance to prolonged exposure and grows on the lower shore just above low tide level. It is a very common wrack that will reach 5 feet in length. It

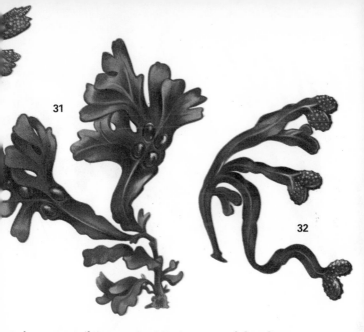

can be very easily recognized by its serrated fronds.

Fucus vesiculosus [31] is the Bladder Wrack, a species occupying the middle shore in the zone above the Toothed Wrack. It grows to about 4 feet in length and is identified by the small air bladders on the fronds. However, these can be absent in plants growing in exposed situations. In parts of Scotland it is called 'Paddy Tang' where it supplements meal used as pig food. *Fucus spiralis* or Spiral Wrack [32] occupies the part of the shore above the Bladder Wrack. It has no air bladders, the fronds are often twisted and the plant is small, growing up to 16 inches long. The receptacles tend to be of a uniform round shape. In parts of Ireland the mucilage from the ripe receptacles is used as a corn cure. *Fucus ceranoides* [33] is the Horned Wrack and is found in fast flowing rivers at their estuaries, growing to 18 inches in length. It can usually be recognized by its small pointed receptacles and fan-shaped lateral fronds that are narrower than the main fronds from which they arise. *Ascophyllum nodosum* [34], or Knotted Wrack often forms extensive growths in sheltered situations where it can grow up to 10

33 *Fucus ceranoides*, Horned Wrack
34 *Ascophyllum nodosum*, Knotted Wrack
35 *Pelvetia canaliculata*, Channelled Wrack
36 *Himanthalia elongata*, Sea Thong

feet in length. It usually occurs on the shore above the Serrated Wrack zone and sometimes competes with Spiral Wrack on the middle shore. The air bladders are conspicuous and as they are sometimes used by children to make whistles the Wrack is also called 'Sea Whistle'.

Pelvetia canaliculata [35] is the Channelled Wrack. This species can withstand considerable periods of dessication and therefore grows on the upper shore extending downwards, sometimes into the Spiral Wrack zone. When left exposed for long periods the plant may become black. In parts of Scotland cattle are often seen grazing on *Pelvetia* where it is called 'Cow Tang'. *Himanthalia elongata*, the Sea Thong, has narrow strap-like fronds arising from an inverted cone-like thallus.

Red Seaweeds (Phylum Rhodophyta)

Porphyra umbilicalis the Purple Laver [37] is a delicate weed of the upper or middle shore, but sometimes growing throughout the intertidal region. It has fronds 6–8 inches in diameter and is prolific from autumn to the following spring on the British coasts. *Gelidium corneum* [38], is a variable species but not common, fringing rock pools on the middle shore. *Cystoclonium purpureum* [39] has bushy fronds that arise from a thallus of 8–12 inches in length and each frond terminates in a fine tip of one cell. This plant inhabits the middle and lower shore and is often found in rock pools. *Phyllophora epiphylla* [40] is a widespread species occurring in deep-water pools. It grows to 6 inches in length and is often found growing among other weeds. It reproduces during the winter. *Ahnfeltia plicata* [41], is a densely tufted wiry plant growing to 6 inches in length and called in France 'Fil de Fer'. It grows on rocks and stones on the middle and lower shore.

Gigartina stellata [42] is abundant on the west coast of the British Isles and occupies regions of the lower shore where it grows in dense colonies. Older plants have minute papillae on the surface of the fronds and these contain the reproductive bodies. This species was once used to make agar for bacteriological laboratories during the war years when normal supplies from Japan were not available.

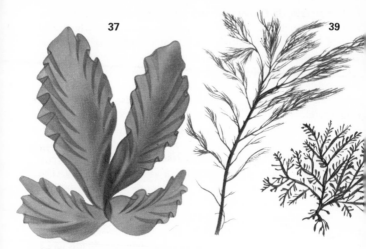

37

39

37 *Porphyra umbilicalis*, Purple Laver
38 *Gelidium corneum*
39 *Cystoclonium purpureum*

Chondrus crispus [43] Carragheen, is a reddish-purple plant but will turn green when exposed to strong sunlight. It also shows considerable variation in shape, with narrow or broad fronds that grow to 3 inches in length and vary from ½ to 1 inch in width. This species is also called 'Irish Moss' and, although not now used for medical purposes, it is still employed for gelling blancmanges. At one time diluted extracts of this seaweed were mixed with cocoa or lemon and were believed to be of some therapeutic value, especially for lung complaints. The word 'carragheen' is perhaps derived from the Irish 'carrigeen' meaning a small rock on which the plant is frequently found growing. Carragheen occurs on the middle shore in rock pools. *Dumontia incrassata* [44] is a seaweed that can reach 14 inches in length and its minute holdfast attaches the plant firmly to stones and rocks in mid-shore pools. It is usually one of the very common annual seaweeds occurring during the spring and early summer. The colour can vary from a deep red, when growing in shaded pools, to a yellowish-green when the plant occurs in sun exposed conditions.

The fronds of *Dilsea carnosa* [45] can reach 15 inches or more in length and up to 5 inches in width. These leathery fronds are shiny and deep red in colour. The young plants usually appear during the autumn, grow throughout the winter and reach maturity during the spring. *Dilsea* is found on many parts of the North European coast and seems more common in the south of the British Isles. In Denmark it is called 'røde klude' meaning 'red rags' and has often been confused with the Dulse, *Rhodymenia palmata* [48].

Corallina officinalis [46] can vary in length from 1 to 5 inches, depending on where it is growing, and its colour can also vary from a pale pink to a deep purple. The stiff upright branches are impregnated with lime and magnesium and these calcareous seaweeds, of which this species is but one example, are quite different in texture and appearance from all the others described here. They in fact bear some resemblance to the animal colonial hydroids (page 58) and until the middle of the last century they were classified with these coelenterates. *C. officinalis* is a very common seaweed and is to be found on most of the rocky shores around the

40 *Phyllophora crispa*
41 *Ahnfeltia plicata*
42 *Gigartina stellata*

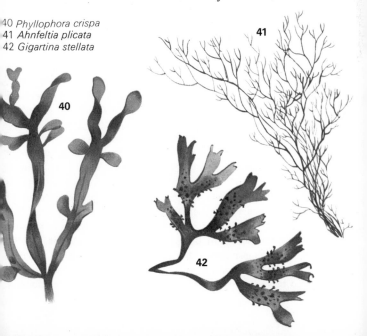

British Isles where it carpets the rock surfaces on the middle and lower beach.

Lomentaria clavellosa [47] grows to 12 inches high and its gelatinous fronds adhere to paper when dried as a herbarium specimen (page 152). It is usually found on the lower shore on rocks and other weeds on many parts of the British coast. *Rhodymenia palmata* [48], or Dulse, is a perennial, growing to 12 inches long, and commonly found attached to fronds of other seaweeds such as the Oarweeds. In Ireland it is called 'Dillisk' and in parts of the British Isles is still dried and used as a substitute for tobacco 'chew'. It can also be used in salads and is grazed by sheep in the north and west of Scotland.

Ceramium rubrum [49] occurs on most shores of the British Isles and varies considerably in shape and colour, from reddish-brown to a greenish-yellow. The tufts can grow to 12 inches high. *Griffithsia flosculosa* [50] is another tufted plant that will grow to 6 inches in length. It is common on the British coasts and may be found growing on the sides of deep rock pools on the more exposed regions of the shore. *Plumaria elegans* [51] grows to about $4\frac{1}{2}$ inches in height and reproduces during the winter months in the south of England. It is usually found in shaded regions and in rock pools of the middle and lower shore.

Hypoglossum woodwardii, [52] a perennial plant growing on other seaweeds and usually found on the lower shore, is fairly common off the English and Scottish coasts and grows to a maximum height of 6 inches. *Delesseria sanguinea* [53], has fronds that can grow to 9 inches long. It is a common form often growing on *Laminaria* species, or attached to rocks in shady positions on the lower shore where it can grow down to a depth of 20 fathoms. *Cryptopleura ramosa* [54], growing to 5 inches high, prefers shady, deep pools on the middle or lower shore. It may be especially abundant in the south of the British Isles. *Nitophyllum punctatum* [55] prefers shady rock pools where it is often found in profusion, sometimes attached to larger species of weeds. The fronds, with their characteristic truncate apices, do not have veins and are delicate, easily tearing when the plant is handled. The fronds often reach 7 inches in length and exceptionally

43 *Chondrus crispus* Carragheen
44 *Dumontia incrassata*
45 *Dilsea carnosa*

46 *Corallina officinalis*
47 *Lomentaria clavellosa*
48 *Rhodymenia palmata,* Dulse

49 *Ceramium rubrum*
50 *Griffithsia flosculosa*
51 *Plumaria elegans*

52 *Hypoglossum woodwardii*
53 *Delesseria sanguinea*
54 *Cryptopleura ramosa*

55 *Nitophyllum punctatum*
56 *Phycodrys rubens*

12 inches. The plant is an annual, reproducing near the end of March. *Phycodrys rubens* [56] is a plant very rich in colour and resembling *Delesseria sanguinea* [53] from which it differs by the paler fronds that grow to about 9 inches in length. The edges of the fronds are much divided and resemble oak leaves from which the generic name *Phycodrys*, meaning 'Seaweed Oak' is derived. This is a common perennial plant usually found in shady situations on the lower shore and often growing on species of *Laminaria*. It reproduces during the spring and summer and makes a very suitable herbarium mount (page 152). *Heterosiphonia plumosa* [57] grows to 8 inches in length, sometimes longer in deeper

water, and many varieties have been noted. It is usually found attached to rocks or to other seaweeds on the lower shore. *Laurencia pinnatifida*, Pepper Dulse, is a variable species, reaches 8 inches in height and its colour can vary from a yellowish-green to a dark red according to its habitat. It is usually found on the mid-shore in rock pools and the plants growing on the upper part of the shore are small, often reaching only 2 inches. It is a perennial species reaching its maximum size during the winter and sexual reproduction occurs about April or May.

Polysiphonia lanosa is a species that occurs on all parts of the British coast where *Ascophyllum nodosum* [34] is found since it grows in dense tufts on the thallus of this latter species. The fronds can reach nearly 2 inches high and sexual reproduction occurs throughout most of the year.

Plankton

The word plankton was used first by the German Zoologist Professor Victor Hensen for those plants and animals that float and drift about in the upper regions of the sea. Such forms may vary from the minute algal plants (phytoplankton) to the larger animals such as the jelly-fishes (zooplankton). Although the more diverse plankton are usually found in off-shore waters or in mid-ocean surface waters, many of the smaller planktonic animals and plants are often left behind in rock pools or on the beaches as the tide ebbs.

The algae of inshore plankton is well represented by the diatoms. These microscopic plants rarely exceed $\frac{1}{50}$ inch in diameter and their cell walls are composed of silica. Diatoms, along with the smaller algae, form the 'grass of the sea' on which many animals 'graze'. These latter, in turn, are eaten by larger marine animals. In contrast to the diatoms the algal dinoflagellates are equipped with two minute whips (flagella) that propel their bodies through the water. Many species are much larger than the diatoms and a few are phosphorescent. Some species of another algal group, the blue-green algae, are sometimes found in inshore waters and they appear as minute thread-like filaments when viewed through a microscope. A related group, the yellow-green algae, are often evident on the beach as slimy gelatinous capsules covering rocks or seaweeds.

60 Collecting plankton in the sub-littoral waters

60

The more obviously recognized animals of the plankton are the larval stages of many of the bottom-dwelling species as well as many of the actively swimming adult forms. The smallest zooplankton dwellers are the Protozoa, which are formed of only a single cell. The most common of the inshore protozoans are the shelled foraminiferans, while the largest animals are usually the jellyfishes.

So that plankton can be studied more closely they can be collected by trawling a net behind a boat in the off-shore waters or in mid-ocean. An excellent account of the methods employed and apparatus used by the biologists for this purpose is given in Dr James Fraser's book *Nature Adrift* (see reference 8). Many planktonic forms, however, can be collected at certain times of the year by pushing a fine muslin hand net through the sub-littoral waters in the manner illustrated in figure 60.

The density and the general distribution of the various forms of plankton in the ocean can tell us a great deal about the distribution of the shoals of fishes that feed on these small floating forms. One of the more important of these fish is the Herring.

The vessel shown in figure 61 is trawling a device known as a 'continuous plankton recorder' that was invented by Professor Alister Hardy as a method for estimating the

61 The continuous plankton recorder in action

61

density and types of plankton in any particular area. This torpedo-shaped device can be towed, unlike a tow-net, at full speed behind the ship and it automatically samples the plankton as it travels. The recorder is equipped with fins that enable it to be towed and also kept at a predetermined depth, thus sampling the plankton at any particular level. As it travels, water enters through a hole at the front end and flows through the machine leaving at the rear. The water that enters is slowed down and plankton is trapped on to a continuously moving band of silk gauze that travels slowly across the tunnel. This band, with its plankton, is then wound into a tank containing a fixative and preservative such as formalin. The movements of the rollers and gears are activated by a propeller on the rear of the machine that is set turning as the recorder is towed through the water. The roll of gauze is eventually covered by another layer of fabric and the plankton is thus sandwiched between the two layers before being finally wound into the storage tank.

In the laboratory, the roll is carefully unwound and the various species of plankton are identified. Their densities are calculated and correlated with the locality and depths of the regions trawled. The continuous plankton recorder was formerly used by herring fishery vessels to estimate the richness of plankton and to locate the shoals of fishes. Echo sounding has now replaced the use of the recorder for this purpose.

Phytoplankton – the diatoms and dinoflagellates

The Phytoplankton belong to the Phyla Chrysophyta (diatoms) and Pyrrophyta (dinoflagellates). The cell wall of a diatom is composed of hard silica and resembles a box, with its deep lid fitting snugly over the box part. The outer surface of the cell wall has minute perforations and many species have elaborate surface sculpturing of the cell wall.

When diatoms die their shells do not disintegrate, as might be expected, but sink slowly to the bottom of the sea where, if there are sufficient numbers present, they will form a 'diatomaceous ooze'. This diatomaceous ooze can be found on the Antarctic and North Pacific sea beds and in these regions it forms a continuous belt.

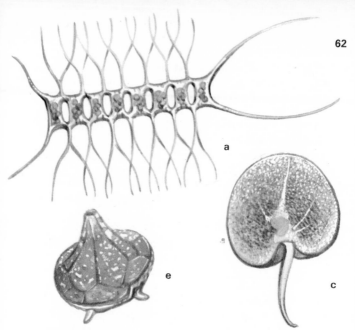

62 A selection of inshore phytoplankton. The diatoms: *a. Chaetoceros decipiens, b. Biddulphia regia,* and dinoflagellates: *c. Noctiluca scintillans,* a phosphorescent species that may be so abundant that it gives the water a 'tomato-soup' appearance; it may be left behind as a red scum on rocks. *d. Ceratium tripos* and *e. Peridinium depressum.* All about × 375

Diatoms, in common with green plants, feed by the process of photosynthesis and also reproduce by cell division, a process known as binnary fission. In some species the cells remain attached to each other, thus forming chains. Throughout this repeated binnary fission many species of diatoms actually become reduced in size, because each new cell becomes only half the size of the former one. Thus, there is often a considerable range in the size of the same species. This reduction, however, usually culminates with the formation of a special body known as an auxospore, that is, a bladder-like mass of protoplasm in which new cell walls of the original size are formed.

Dinoflagellates, in contrast to diatoms, can live in waters less rich in nutrient salts as they can absorb organic food

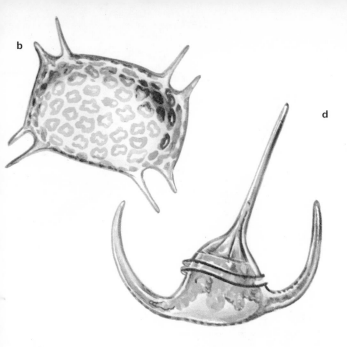

b

d

particles in addition to using the photosynthetic method of feeding. Some of the more common species of diatoms and dinoflagellates found in the inshore waters are shown in figure 62. The diatom *Biddulphia regia* is now one of the commonest diatoms in European waters and occurs often in dense concentrations. The dinoflagellate *Noctiluca scintillans* can produce a brilliant phosphorescence that gives the water a ghostly blue colour when this species is abundant. The species *Ceratium tripos* [62*d*] and related forms are often plentiful in plankton samples taken in the autumn. *Ceratium* and *Peridinium* are also phosphorescent species.

Zooplankton – the foraminiferans

The smallest forms of zooplankton are the protozoans (Phylum Protozoa). Of these, the sub-class Foraminifera, meaning hole bearers, are usually well represented on certain types of shore. Each individual animal is enveloped in a shell made of calcium carbonate and, similarly to the diatoms, the 'skeletal' remains sink to the bottom of the ocean when its

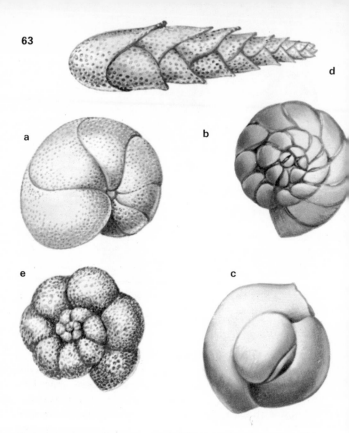

63

living content dies. In parts of the Atlantic Ocean the sea bed is composed almost entirely of these dead shells. This grey muddy deposit is chiefly composed of shell belonging to the genus *Globigerina* and is called 'Globigerinan ooze'. Although living foraminiferans are encountered in plankton hauls or in shore sand samples, their dead shells are easily picked out of beach deposits using a low power microscope or a high power hand-lens. Figure 63 shows a selection of such foraminiferans found in the sand deposits of Selsey Bill, Sussex, a region that was intensively studied by the two biologists E. Heron-Allen and A. Earland. The cliffs on the right of the figure contain the shells of many fossil species. Cliff erosion by wave action (page 12) will wash these shells into the sea where they will mingle with the dead shells of recent living species and form a part of the sandy beach.

Among the conspicuous and more delicate forms of zooplankton are the minute jellyfish stages of colonial sedentary Cnidarians belong to the class hydroza (page 58). One form, *Phialidium hemisphaericum* is, in fact, the jellyfish stage of the hydroid *Clytia johnstoni*. Similar to its larger or smaller relatives it is very carnivorous, catching and eating young fishes. Also common in the inshore plankton are the Sea Gooseberries or Ctenophores that luminesce at night, while the Arrow Worms or Chaetognathes occur chiefly in the off-shore plankton. Perhaps the most prominent plankton dwellers are the crustaceans, several examples of which are shown in figure 64.

Many planktonic animals will only rise towards the surface at night and sink into deeper waters during the day. They are said to exhibit vertical migration. Many factors influence this migration, the most important perhaps is the adjustment of the various species to a light intensity most suitable for them. The lower waters often flow in a different direction to the surface waters and thus often change the course of the plankton. These repeated changes of direction enable the animals to vary their feeding grounds and to explore new environments.

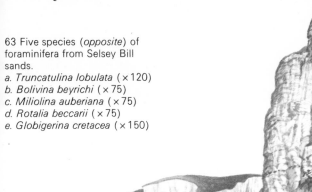

63 Five species (*opposite*) of foraminifera from Selsey Bill sands.
a. *Truncatulina lobulata* (×120)
b. *Bolivina beyrichi* (×75)
c. *Miliolina auberiana* (×75)
d. *Rotalia beccarii* (×75)
e. *Globigerina cretacea* (×150)

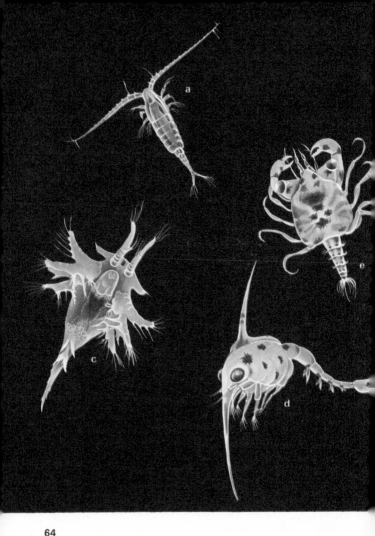

64

64 The small crustaceans predominant in shore plankton :

a. *Calanus finmarchicus* (copepod)
b. Larva of *Crangon vulgaris* (Brown Shrimp), both $\frac{1}{16}$ inch
c. Larva (nauplius) of *Balanus balanoides* (Common Barnacle) $\frac{1}{16}$ inch
d. The zoeal and e. megalopa stages of *Carcinus maenas*

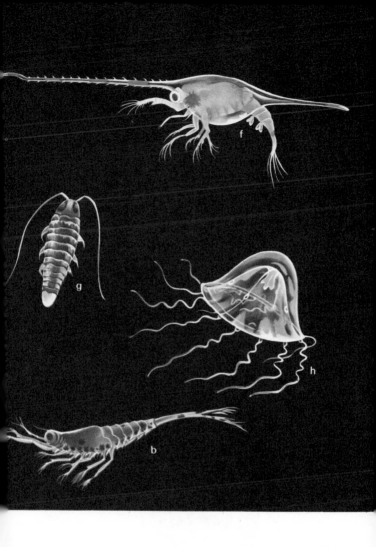

(Shore Crab) $\frac{1}{8}$ inch
f. Zoea of *Porcellana longicornis*
(Porcelain Crab) $\frac{1}{8}$ inch
g. *Eurydice pulchra* (isopod)
$\frac{1}{4}$ inch
The medusa stages of many
hydrozoans (page 59) are
found in the plankton
h. The medusa called 'Phialidium
hemisphaericum', the floating
stage of the hydroid *Clytia
johnstoni* $\frac{1}{2}$ inch

65

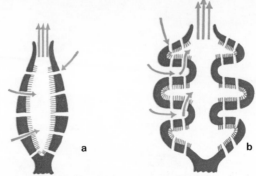

65 Organization of *a.* simple sponge; *b.* more advanced type

Sponges (Phylum Porifera)

Sponges are usually evident as encrusting masses or projections growing on rock surfaces or larger seaweeds. Because of their apparent vegetative appearance and lack of structure, they were once classified as plants until the naturalist John Ellis showed their true animal relationships.

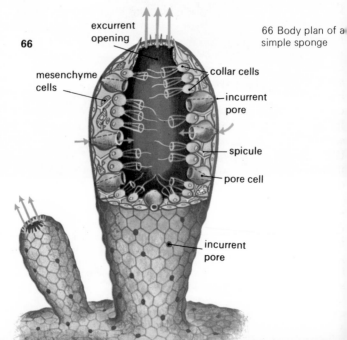

66 Body plan of a simple sponge

A typical sponge is composed of a mass of cells organized into a colony and permeated by canals through which water flows. Sponge colonies can be graded according to their complexity of canal structure [65]. The general organization of a sponge is shown in figure 66 and a part of the body wall has been cut away to show the internal structure at high magnification. The minute incurrent pores are the external openings of the pore cells through which water enters the body cavity. The motion of this water is assisted by the beating of the flagellate collar cells and the water leaves through the excurrent opening. Small particles of food, carried into the sponge by the water, stick to the collar cells and are engulfed. The mesenchyme cells move around in the jelly-like material and secrete the spicules that are the supporting framework of the body. They also help to digest and transport food.

In many sponges these spicules are composed of calcium carbonate but, in some, they are of silica. One group has a supporting framework of a horny substance called spongin.

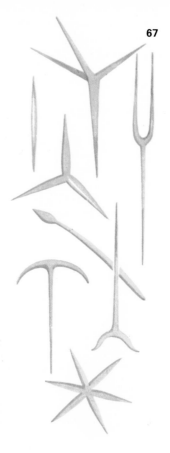

67 Calcareous and siliceous sponge spicules. Spicules vary in shape. Calcareous ones are often three-rayed, while siliceous types are four or six-rayed. Many siliceous species extrude them continuously from the body surface. It is thought that spicule formation is a method by which the sponge excretes unwanted calcium or silica.

The commonest method by which sponges reproduce, is vegetative budding or branching. Figure 68 shows some examples of how this occurs in *Grantia*, the Purse Sponge. In *a–c* is shown how constrictions appear about the middle of the colony and the two halves separate. Buds may appear around the edge of the colony as shown in *d* or the whole sponge can fragment as depicted in *e*.

Sponges also reproduce by sexual means and then eggs and sperms are produced. These are formed in the same individual in some species while others have separate sexes. After the egg cell has been fertilized [69a] it soon grows into a many celled embryo [b] enclosed in a capsule and embedded in the body wall of the parent sponge. This embryo eventually bursts through the wall of the nearest excurrent opening and is swept out of the body. It now swims using its many flagella. This larva [c] with its many mesenchyme cells and

68 Vegetative reproduction of sponges

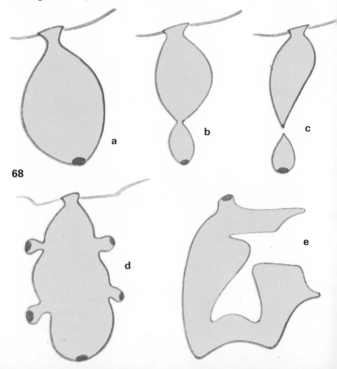

68

69

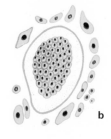

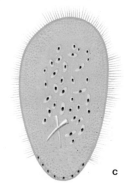

a few spicules, soon settles on to a suitable surface and changes into a flat, semi-transparent platelet [d] that can move slowly over the substrata until a small pore appears on its upper surface. Branches are then sent out [e] and a new colony is established. In some encrusting species hundreds of these small larvae settle near each other and may join to form a continuous layer covering many square yards of rock surface.

There are about 230 species of sponges that are known to occur in British waters and many of these inhabit the lower shore down to the littoral zone. Of the three classes composing the phylum Porifera only two, the classes Calcarea and Desmospongiae are represented on British shores. As the name implies the Calcarea have carbonate spicules that will dissolve by boiling a piece of the sponge in a weak solution of hydrochloric acid and water. The Desmospongiae have siliceous spicules or spongin for their skeletons.

69 Sexual reproduction

70 Some common species of sponges grouped on a rock surface

a. Grantia compressa, Purse Sponge, which grows 2 inches on lower shore
b. Leucosolenia coriacea, one of a group of closely related variable coloured species and *c. Halichondria bowerbanki,* a Breadcrumb Sponge both 3–4 inches

d. Adocia cineria and *e.* a portion of the colony at a much higher magnification
f. Ophilitaspongia seriata 2 inches
g. Suberites domuncula 3 inches
h. The shell of *Crepidula* Slipper Limpet bearing the small holes bored by the sponge *Cliona celata*

Cnidarians (Phylum Cnidaria or Coelenterata)

Although the jellyfishes and anemones are the most familiar examples of members of this phylum, the smaller and much less conspicuous hydroids that are found growing on seaweeds and on rock surfaces, are very easily overlooked. The word 'coelenterata' is often used for this phylum and it means 'hollow guts' a term that aptly describes the basic body structure of these animals. The body structure, in fact, consists of a sac-like digestive cavity with a single opening illustrated in diagrammatic form in figure 71a and also in figure 79. The term 'cnidaria' however, refers to their most characteristic feature. This is the thread or 'stinging' cells, which are called nematocysts, with which all the cnidarians are equipped [72, a–b].

The basic body plan of a cnidarian can assume one of two forms as are shown in the diagrams below. Figure 71 a shows a fixed polyp that is attached by its lower end to a firm surface such as a rock, while figure 71 b illustrates a medusa form that is a mere inversion of the polyp but which is free-swimming. Both these forms alternate in the life cycles of many species.

The phylum Cnidaria is composed of three classes: Class Hydrozoa, the Sea Firs or hydroids; Class Scyphozoa, which are the true jellyfishes and Class Anthozoa (Actinozoa), which contains the Sea Anemones and Corals. These are described from page 59 to 69.

71 The cnidarian body plan

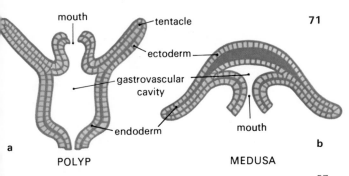

71

POLYP

MEDUSA

a

b

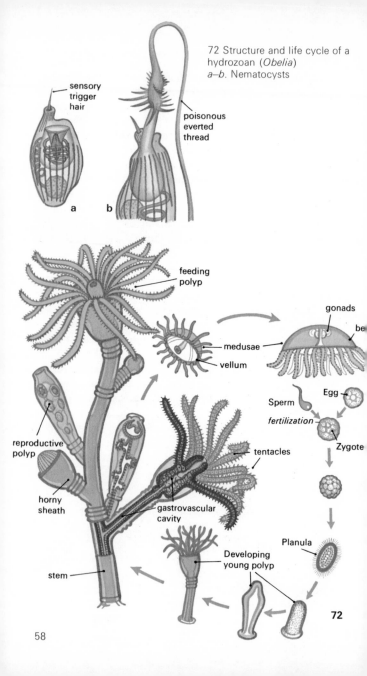

72 Structure and life cycle of a hydrozoan (*Obelia*)
a–b. Nematocysts

sensory trigger hair

poisonous everted thread

a

b

feeding polyp

medusae

vellum

gonads

be

reproductive polyp

horny sheath

tentacles

gastrovascular cavity

stem

Sperm

Egg

fertilization

Zygote

Planula

Developing young polyp

72

58

Class Hydrozoa

Figure 72 shows part of a colony of the hydrozoan *Obelia*. The colony feeds by catching small animals using the numerous thread cells (nematocysts) that are embedded in the tentacles of the feeding polyp. A nematocyst cell, highly magnified, is shown in *a*. The cell awaits a stimulus of its sensory trigger hair and, when this is touched by a passing animal, the coiled thread is everted with an explosive force as shown in *b*. Many of these threads will penetrate into the surface of an animal and, as they have hollow shafts, a paralysing poison can be injected into the prey.

Threads of other cells will then curl around the prey and entangle it while a further type have adhesive tips, which stick to the struggling prey. These nematocysts are packed very close together in batteries embedded in the tentacles and the trapped prey is thus immobilized and slowly drawn towards the mouth by the tentacles before passing into the gastrovascular cavity, where it is digested. This cavity is a continuous structure throughout the whole of the colony. The delicate polyps are protected by a horny sheath into which they can withdraw.

The usual method of asexual reproduction is by budding of new polyps from the stems, but at certain times during the year the reproductive polyps give rise to minute saucer-shaped medusae. A series of these developing medusae is shown in the two reproductive polyps in figure 72. Each fully developed medusa is eventually budded off from the apex of the polyp and escapes into the sea where it floats in the surface waters.

The medusa has a mouth, a gastrovascular cavity and canals. It feeds in the same manner as the polyp stage using its batteries of nematocysts embedded in the ring of tentacles. It is this medusa, resembling a minute jellyfish, that provides the sexual stage in the life cycle of *Obelia*. Hanging from the middle of the inner side of the swimming bell of the medusa are the gonads and it is these that produce either sperms or eggs in individual medusae. These eggs and sperms are shed into the water, often at the same time, by numerous medusae that are present in the same area and the fertilization of many of the egg cells is, therefore, assured.

Each fertilized egg is called a zygote and this develops into a minute larva, (planula), that has its surface covered with short hairs or 'cilia'. The planula will eventually settle on to a rock surface and, if conditions are right, grows into a new polyp. It is this passive but mobile medusa stage in the life cycle of *Obelia* that spreads the animal to new localities.

In contrast to the fixed forms, some hydrozoans are composed of floating colonies that dwell in the upper regions of the sea. Such forms are represented by the order Siphonophora. An example is *Physalia physalia* the Portuguese Man-O-War [77]. This hydrozoan appears at first sight to resemble a true jellyfish but close inspection will show that it has no swimming bell [78] and is propelled by wind pressure against its gas filled bladder that protrudes above the water surface. This bladder is thought to be a modified medusa that has lost its swimming ability. From this bladder hangs a mass of highly modified polyps all specialized for various functions. Some have very long tentacles heavily armed with nematocysts. These form the 'drift nets' of the colony and when a fish or other passing animal touches these tentacles it is quickly paralysed by the discharged nematocysts. These are so potent that they can easily immobilize a fully grown mackerel. The prey is drawn up towards the floating colony and another group of polyps proceeds to digest the catch. Other polyps are concerned with the reproduction of the colony.

The Portuguese Man-O-War is an impressive animal about 6 inches long and with tentacles that can reach up to 60 feet in length. Although it is normally an inhabitant of the open sea, strong prevailing southerly winds have been known to drive numbers of them close inshore where they can cause great discomfort if bathers happen to be stung by their powerful nematocysts.

73–76 Four common British hydrozoans belonging to order Hydroida
73 *Coryne pusilla*
74 *Clava multicornis* (*a* in each case shows the natural size of the species and *b* individuals at high magnification)
75 *Hydractinia echinata*, common on Whelk shell inhabited by *Pagurus berhardus*, Hermit Crab
76 *Tubularia indivisa* (× 5)

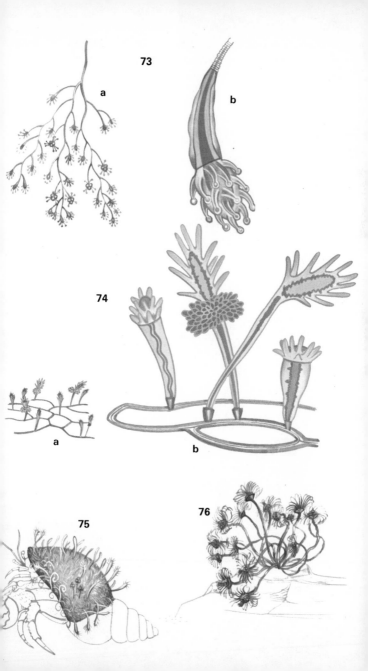

73

a

b

74

a

b

75

76

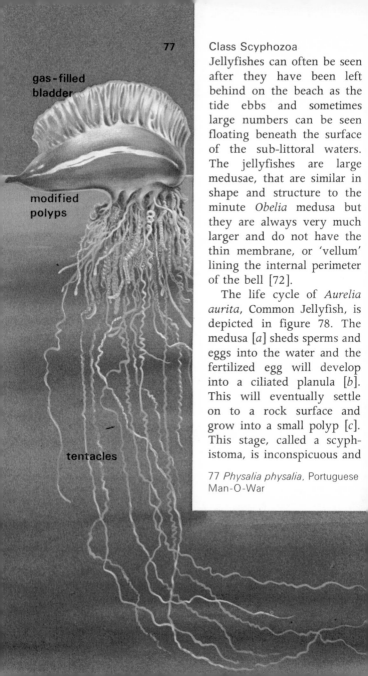

gas-filled
bladder

modified
polyps

tentacles

Class Scyphozoa

Jellyfishes can often be seen after they have been left behind on the beach as the tide ebbs and sometimes large numbers can be seen floating beneath the surface of the sub-littoral waters. The jellyfishes are large medusae, that are similar in shape and structure to the minute *Obelia* medusa but they are always very much larger and do not have the thin membrane, or 'vellum' lining the internal perimeter of the bell [72].

The life cycle of *Aurelia aurita*, Common Jellyfish, is depicted in figure 78. The medusa [a] sheds sperms and eggs into the water and the fertilized egg will develop into a ciliated planula [b]. This will eventually settle on to a rock surface and grow into a small polyp [c]. This stage, called a scyphistoma, is inconspicuous and

77 *Physalia physalia*, Portuguese Man-O-War

never colonial like *Obelia*. As it matures horizontal constrictions appear as shown in [d] and these deepen until small medusa jellyfishes are budded off [e]. A juvenile jellyfish is known as an ephyra that will grow into a large medusa and begin the life cycle over again.

The adult jellyfish has its nematocysts implanted in the four trailing mouth lobes and these lead into a stomach, from which arise four pouches. These can easily be located because their walls are lined with purple-coloured ovaries or testes. An elaborate system of canals serves to carry digested food to every part of the body as well as the respiratory gases. Around the edge of the umbrella are eight sense organs called tentaculocysts and each of these consists of a minute calcareous nodule that is enclosed in a sheath of cells invested with sensory processes. This structure hangs from the wall of a cavity formed from one of the canals and can come to rest against any part of the canal wall depending on which way the jellyfish is tilted. It thus appears to act as a form of balancing organ and, assisted by the minute light-sensitive cells near the tentaculocysts, controls the direction of movement in *Aurelia*. Such organs are also developed in many other medusae.

78 Life cycle of *Aurelia aurelia*, Common Jellyfish

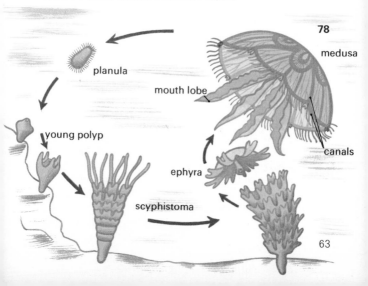

Aurelia is best observed in the shallow sea where its swimming movements, which are effected by a slow pulsation of the swimming bell, are very easily seen. This movement drives water in and out of the bell concavity and the animal is therefore propelled in the opposite direction to that of the expelled water.

Although *Aurelia* is adequately equipped to catch small fish, it would seem that the larger specimens in fact appear to feed on small planktonic animals, such as copepods and the larvae of crustaceans. Professor J. H. Orton in 1922 observed that *Aurelia* could trap these minute planktonic forms in a sticky mucus that covers the upper and lower surfaces of the bell. This mucus is constantly moving towards the mouth driven by the numerous cilia lining the grooves of the mouth lobes.

Class Anthozoa

The anemones are sometimes called anthozoans meaning 'flower animals' as they show best another characteristic of the cnidaria, that of radial design, in which the body plan radiates similarly to the spokes of a wheel and resembles superficially the radial pattern of flowers. Identification of sea anemones is difficult and often depends on a very technical dissection. Colours and shapes are extremely variable and individuals of the same species often seem to vary one from another.

Figure 79 shows an anemone with a part of the body wall cut away to reveal the internal structure. The muscular body is attached to a rock by a basal disc on which the anemone can move slowly. This disc anchors the body so firmly that attempts to remove it from its rock often only result in tearing the body. The hollow tentacles, surrounding the mouth, are well-endowed with nematocysts and the gullet leads into a gastrovascular cavity that contains a complicated series of vertical partitions, that serve to increase the digestive surface area. There is also a well-developed nerve net extending throughout the body, but this has only a slow response to external stimuli. The longitudinal and circular muscles enable the body to be greatly extended in some species and can similarly bring about a high degree of contraction. In this latter state the anemone can resist a certain amount of drying out when exposed at low tide.

Anemones reproduce by budding and an individual will divide into two or more smaller specimens. Sexual reproduction also occurs, however, and the eggs and sperms that are produced by the ovaries and testes, (which are situated on the walls of the gastrovascular partitions) are ejected through the mouth. A fertilized egg will develop into a small, free-swimming planula that settles on to a rock and grows into a new anemone.

Three orders of the class Anthozoa are represented on the shore. These are the order Actinaria, which comprises the sea anemones and has already been referred to, the order Alcyonacea, the soft corals and the order Scleractinia, which includes the stony corals.

79 Structure of an anthozoan (anemone)

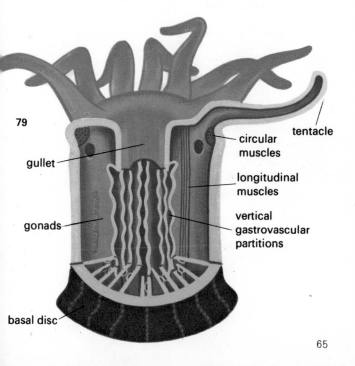

80 Order Actinaria, some
British Anemones of the
shore
a. *Metridium senile*,
Plumose Anemone, four
on pier piles, or rock crev
on lower shore, 5 inches
b. Colour varieties of
Actinia equina, Beadlet
Anemone, abundant on
the middle and lower
shore, 2 inches
c. *Tealia felina*, Dahlia
Anemone has a warty
body often covered with
pieces of concealing grav
and is common on the
lowest shore. 2 inches
d. *Adamsia palliata*, base
of this species is usually

rapped around Whelk
ell occupied by Hermit
ab, *Pagurus prideauxi*
d occurs where hermits
e exposed at low tide
Sagartia elegans, has
merous varieties
d is abundant on lower
ore. 2 inches high
Anemonia sulcata,
akelock's Anemone is
und on west and south
asts, shallow pools,
ddle and lower shore
Bunodactis verrucosa,
artlet or Gem Anemone
found in lower shore
ck pools or cracks
der stones on West
asts. 2 inches high

81 *Alcyonium digitatum*, Dead Men's Fingers
82 Structure of the ctenophore, *Pleurobrachia*

83 *Pleurobrachia pileus*, Sea Gooseberry, ¾ inch
84 *Beroe cucumis*, 2 inches long

A representative of the order Alcyonacea that occurs in British coastal waters is *Alcyonium digitatum*, also known as Dead Men's Fingers. This is a colonial anthozoan and when immersed in water the numerous and delicate polyps, each with eight feathery tentacles, can be seen to arise from the finger-shaped fleshy projections. These projections vary in colour from white to yellow, pink or orange, but when it is out of the water they are flesh-coloured, thus giving rise to its common name. The supporting matrix of the colony consists of a jelly-like substance in which calcium carbonate spicules are embedded.

The outline of one of these minute polyps is illustrated in figure 81 *b* at a high magnification. Colonies of Dead Men's Fingers are often found attached to pier piles or in sheltered places attached to rocks on the lower shore where they may grow to 6 inches in length. It is comparatively well distributed around the coast of Britain and can become very common indeed in some localities.

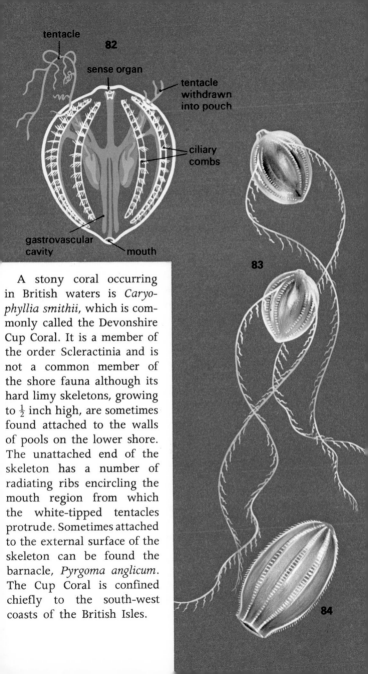

82

tentacle

sense organ

tentacle withdrawn into pouch

ciliary combs

gastrovascular cavity

mouth

83

84

A stony coral occurring in British waters is *Caryo-phyllia smithii*, which is commonly called the Devonshire Cup Coral. It is a member of the order Scleractinia and is not a common member of the shore fauna although its hard limy skeletons, growing to $\frac{1}{2}$ inch high, are sometimes found attached to the walls of pools on the lower shore. The unattached end of the skeleton has a number of radiating ribs encircling the mouth region from which the white-tipped tentacles protrude. Sometimes attached to the external surface of the skeleton can be found the barnacle, *Pyrgoma anglicum*. The Cup Coral is confined chiefly to the south-west coasts of the British Isles.

Ctenophores (Phylum Ctenophora)

Ctenophores are often found in the inshore plankton or sometimes stranded on the beach at ebb tide where they look like lumps of transparent jelly. They were once classified as a sub-phylum of the Cnidaria but are now placed in a phylum of their own chiefly on account of their lack of nematocysts. Figure 82 depicts the general structure of the ctenophore *Pleurobrachia sp*. The most obvious feature is the lines of ciliary combs arranged in rows on the surface of the body, which are used for swimming. The tentacles, that can withdraw into pouches, are armed with spirally wound lasso-cells that produce a sticky substance entangling the prey as the tentacles are looped through the water.

The mouth leads to a branched gastrovascular cavity and the small sense organ seems to function as a balancing device. A nerve net extends throughout the body and co-ordinates the beating of the ciliary lobes. Each specimen has both male and female reproductive organs embedded in the walls of the gastrovascular cavity. Eggs and sperms are shed into the water and the free-swimming larvae soon develop into forms resembling their parents.

The phylum Ctenophora is divided into two orders, the Tentaculata to which the species *Pleurobrachia pileus* [83] belongs and the order Nuda represented by *Beroe cucumis* [84]. Both species are common in British coastal waters.

Flatworms (Phylum Platyhelminthes)

The flatworms or platyhelminthes are represented on the shore by the class Turbellaria, species of which are found among weed in rock pools or moving slowly over the surfaces of rocks and stones. The typical structure of a marine turbellarian is shown in figure 85 for *Leptoplana tremellaris*. The worm glides along by the beating of the numerous fine cilia that cover its external surface. At times

85 *Leptoplana tremellaris*, showing internal structure
86 *Prostheceraeus vittatus*, under stones on the lower shore, 1 inch
87 *Procerodes littoralis*. Often common where freshwater flows over beach, $\frac{3}{4}$ inch long

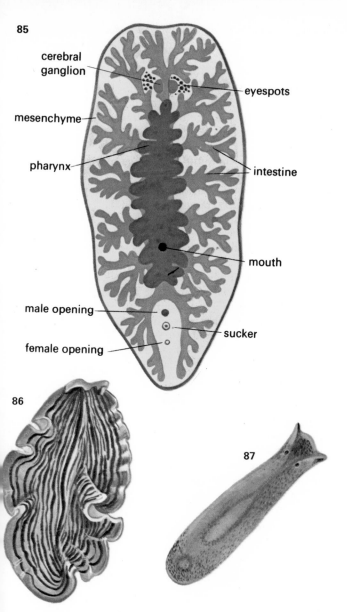

85

cerebral ganglion

eyespots

mesenchyme

pharynx

intestine

mouth

male opening

sucker

female opening

86

87

it may be seen to swim by rapid and successive ripples that pass down the body from front to rear. *Leptoplana* feeds nocturnally, chiefly on polychaet worms (page 76). The elongate muscular pharynx can be extruded through the mouth and provides the exit for the digestive juices that are poured out to begin the external digestion of the captured prey. Partly digested, the food is drawn into the branched intestine that ensures the distribution of nutrients throughout the body.

The flatworms show the beginnings of a central nervous system with the nerve cells concentrated into a bilobed brain, the cerebral ganglion, and two long nerve cords running backwards through the middle body tissue, (or mesenchyme). The eyespots can respond to the direction of light and *Leptoplana* will move away from regions of very high light intensities. The sucker assists the worm to attach to surfaces.

The platyhelminthes are hermaphrodites, which means that each animal has a set of male and female reproductive organs that open on the external surface by small pores. Cross fertilization takes place by two worms pairing and exchanging their reproductive cells. The fertilized eggs hatch as small planktonic larvae that eventually settle and change into small worms resembling their parents.

Proboscis or Ribbon Worms (Phylum Nemertina)

These worms are thin unsegmented forms with the ability of great extension and contraction, thus varying the length of their body considerably. Figure 88 shows the internal structure of a common shore species *Amphiporus lactifloreus*. Unlike the flatworms, the digestive system has, in addition to a mouth, an anus through which unwanted matter is

88 Internal structure of *Amphiporus lactifloreus*, proboscis worm
89 A pilidium larva of a proboscis worm
90–92 Three common shore dwelling proboscis worms of the lower shore

90 *Lineus longissimus*, Bootlace Worm, variable length, but 15 foot is common
91 *Lineus ruber*, maximum length about 9 inches
92 *Amphiporus lactifloreus*, 3 inches

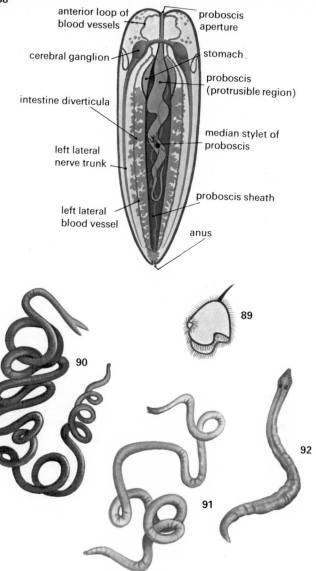

88

anterior loop of blood vessels

proboscis aperture

cerebral ganglion

stomach

proboscis (protrusible region)

intestine diverticula

median stylet of proboscis

left lateral nerve trunk

left lateral blood vessel

proboscis sheath

anus

89

90

91

92

expelled. The ribbon worms have developed a simple blood circulatory system and the blood cells in some species contain haemoglobin – the oxygen carrier of the blood. Nemertines are carnivorous and will feed on annelid worms (page 76). The prey is captured using the proboscis. This is normally retracted within a sheath in the body. The anterior part of the proboscis can be rapidly extruded and wrapped around the prey that is subdued by the copious sticky secretion poured over it. The proboscis of *Amphiporus* is armed with stylets that can penetrate the prey, enabling poisonous fluids to be injected into its body. Digested food is eventually fed into the numerous intestine diverticula and absorbed by the body tissues.

A nemertine may be either a male or female. At breeding time the sex cells are shed into the water and a fertilized egg develops into a minute larva called a pilidium. The young worm slowly develops within the larval skin and when it finally settles on the sea bed it takes up the sedentary life similar to its parents.

Roundworms (Phylum Aschelminthes)

The Aschelminthes are represented on the shore by the class Nematoda. Because of their small size, rarely exceeding $\frac{1}{8}$ inch, they are easily overlooked. Many nematodes are internal parasites of animals and plants but there are numerous free-living species to be found in both soil and water and they are often very common members of the shore sand and mud. Samples of beach deposits often contain innumerable specimens that may become apparent by the active wriggling of their slender bodies forming a figure-of-eight pattern as they move.

The internal structure is not easy to see but figure 93 shows some of the more conspicuous organs. The body wall is composed of an almost impermeable cuticle that is shed from time to time as the worm grows. The buccal cavity leads into a fore-gut and then into an alimentary canal the mid-gut of which is shown in the figure. Undigested food passes out at the anus. The vacuoles are fluid-filled spaces and this fluid is moved by the worm's twisting movements and functions as a primitive type of circulation that distributes food and oxygen.

The sexes are separate and eggs produced by the ovary of the female are fertilized by the male while they are still within the body. The eggs are then passed to the exterior through a genital pore and eventually hatch into juveniles that moult several times before assuming the shape of the adult.

Most of the free-living nematodes are very difficult to identify but some of them are parasitic on sea weeds. The wart-like swellings that are often seen on the fronds of *Ascophyllum nodosum*, Knotted Wrack (page 33) often contain specimens of the worm *Tylenchus spp.*

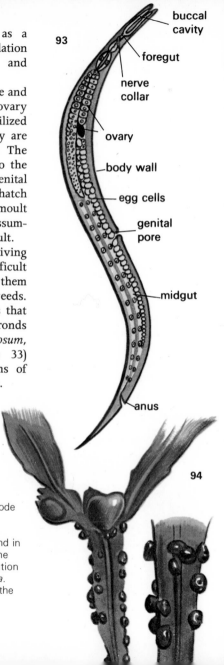

93

buccal cavity

foregut

nerve collar

ovary

body wall

egg cells

genital pore

midgut

anus

94

93 (*Above*) The internal structure of a female nematode worm
94 (*Right*) The nematode, *Tylenchus spp.* is often found in the wart like swellings on the Knotted Wrack. The distribution of these warts is shown in *a.* and an enlarged portion of the thallus in *b.*

Bristle or Polychaet Worms (Phylum Annelida)

An exposed sandy or muddy shore leaves little shelter or places for the attachment of marine plants and animals. Many inhabitants of this type of habitat have attained security, however, by burrowing downwards into the beach that affords some protection against wave action and predators. Of all the burrowing invertebrates, the annelid worms, of the phylum Annelida, belonging to the class Polychaeta are by far the most common of the inhabitants of the sandy and muddy beaches.

An example of a polychaet, or 'many bristled', worm is *Nereis virens*, a Ragworm [95]. This species can reach a length of 3 feet. *Nereis* moves in a characteristic undulating fashion over a muddy surface and the body is composed of numerous rings or segments, a feature typical of all annelids. From this particular feature the name of the phylum is derived; the Latin *annulus* meaning 'a ring'. Most of the segments behind the head have a pair of lobed-shaped paddles (parapodia) that are beset with short bristles or chaetae. These parapodia assist the worm to swim and the chaetae can grip the walls of the burrows in which the worm lives.

Nereis catches its food by everting a pharynx that bears two strong horny jaws. These seize the food that usually

95 *Nereis virens*, a Ragworm

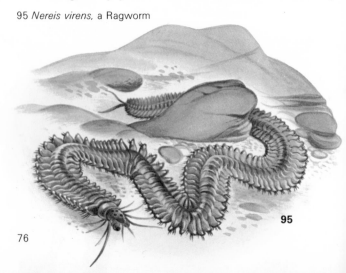

95

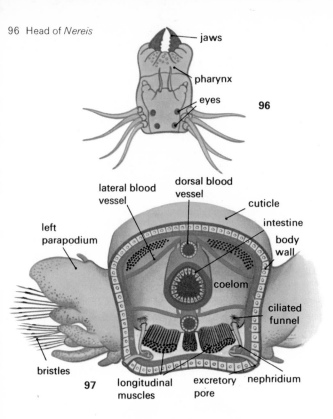

96

97 Structure of a body segment of a polychaet worm

consists of plant and animal remains. The structure of the head showing the four eyes and the everted pharynx bearing these hook-shaped jaws is depicted in figure 96.

The anatomy of one of the segments of *Nereis* is illustrated in figure 97. Repartition of the body parts, particularly of nerves and excretory organs, occurs in nearly every segment of the body and is a typical annelidan feature. The body plan shows advance to that of the Nemertine type especially in the development of a large fluid-filled body space called the coelom, that occupies the region between the intestine and the body wall.

The parapodia are well-supplied with blood capillaries forming efficient areas for respiratory exchange of oxygen and carbon dioxide, carried by the blood haemoglobin. This latter substance is dissolved in the blood instead of being carried in the blood cells. In addition to this, the walls of the dorsal blood vessels can rhythmically contract and relax pumping the blood along the vessels. Waste products, other than carbon dioxide, accumulate in the coelomic fluid and are removed through the ciliated funnels and passed out of the body through the excretory pores of the excretory organs, which are called nephridia. Beneath the almost impervious cuticle are layers of circular and longitudinal muscles that are used to assist the body movements of the worm.

At certain times during the year reproductive cells are budded off from the internal linings of the body cavity of

98

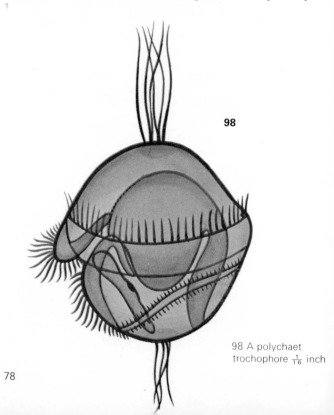

98 A polychaet
trochophore $\frac{1}{16}$ inch

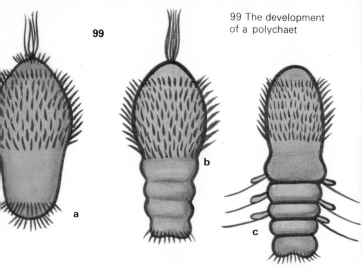

a

b

c

these worms. This process generally occurs in most of the
segments. In some species of *Nereis* large numbers of the
animals swarm near the surface of the sea, the males often
arriving first to await the females. Eggs and sperms are shed
into the water, where fertilization will take place. When
Nereis hatches from the egg it has already passed through
its larval stage within the egg itself.

In some of the species of polychaetes, however, such as
Phyllodoce, this larval trochophore, as it is called, can be
found free-swimming in the plankton. A typical annelidan
trochophore is depicted in figure 98 and because it resembles
the veliger larva, the stage through which many of the
molluscs pass [167], it is thought that both the annelids and
the molluscs have derived from the same ancestral stock in
the remote past.

The development of a typical polychaet trochophore is
illustrated in figure 99. The body of the larva elongates in
the manner depicted in figure 99 *a* and constrictions appear
[*b*] that eventually develop into segments [*c*], while the upper
part of the trochophore grows into the head region. After
this stage, however, the worm settles on to the sea bed to
complete its development.

Figure 100 shows a reconstruction of a section through a sloping middle and lower sandy beach at low tide to show several of the species of polychaet worms in their natural habitats. There is no well established classification for the polychaetes but they are often arranged into two groups; the errant species (Errantia), that are all equipped with a protrusible pharynx and a pair of jaws and live active wandering lives, and the tubicolous sedentary species (Sedentaria), which are without protrusible pharynx or jaws. Nearly all the species belonging to this group construct and live in permanent tubes.

Of the errant species *Nereis diversicolor* [a] burrows slowly downwards through the loose wet sand as the tide recedes. This Ragworm grows to 4 inches and is often found in regions of low salinity particularly on estuarine muddy sand. Its yellowish-brown body, edged with green and with a thin red line, the course of a blood vessel down its back, serves to distinguish it from other species of *Nereis*. *Nephthys hom-*

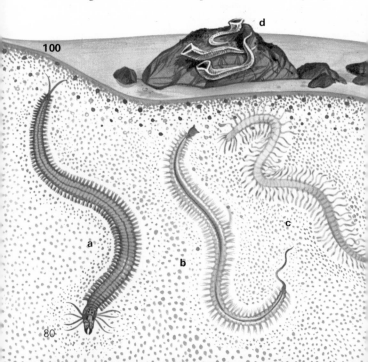

bergi [*b*], the Catworm, grows to 5 inches and is often abundant on sandy gravel. Of the many species of Syllid worms (family Syllidae) the species depicted here is *Syllis prolifera* [*c*]. It is often found beneath stones of the middle shore where it grows to 2 inches.

Of the sedentary tubicolous species the most common on many beaches are the triangular-keeled, white, 3 inch tubes of *Pomatoceros triqueter* [*d*]. This worm builds its tubes on stones and flat rocks. When immersed in water the open ends are capped with crowns of tentacles as the worms emerge. The small mounds of coiled sand interspaced with holes [*e*] identify the habitat of *Arenicola marina,* the Lug-worm, [106] while the smooth tubes of mud or sand that protrude 2 to 3 inches above the sand surface are the homes of the Fan or Peacock Worms of the family Sabellidae. The two specimens shown in figure 100 [*f*] are *Sabella pavonina,* common on the lower shore where they grow to 2 feet. When fully extended their tentacles are a striking colour.

100 Shore dwelling polychaets

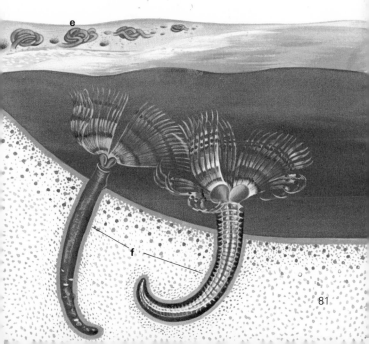

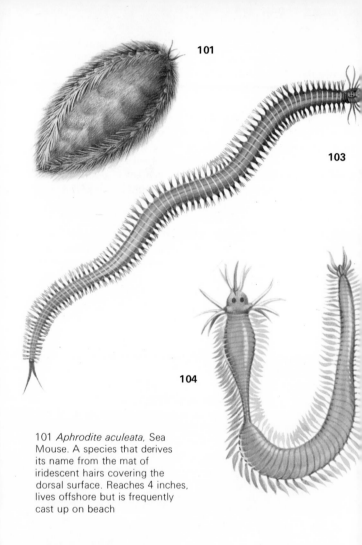

101 *Aphrodite aculeata*, Sea Mouse. A species that derives its name from the mat of iridescent hairs covering the dorsal surface. Reaches 4 inches, lives offshore but is frequently cast up on beach

102 *Harmothoë impar*. The paired scales cover the whole length of the body. It is often found among seaweeds or beneath rocks where it grows to 1 inch in length

103 *Nereis pelagica*, Ragworm. Inhabits middle and lower shore. Small forms often found on *Laminaria* fronds. Grows to 4 inches

104 *Eulalia sanguinea*, Paddle-worm. Usually very active when disturbed from under stones on the lower shore. Reaches about 2 inches in length

106 *Arenicola marina*, Lugworm. A burrower in muddy sand. Fishermen are often seen digging for this species as it is used for bait. The worm builds U-shaped tubes as shown in *a*.

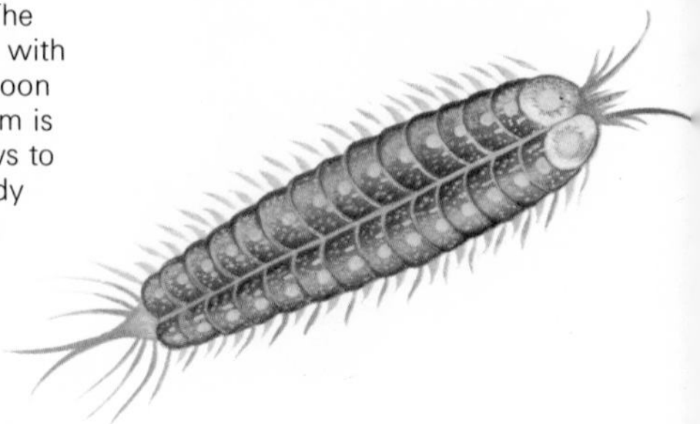

105 *Amphitrite johnstoni*. The tube of this species is lined with a thin layer of mucus that soon disintegrates when the worm is removed. This species grows to 12 inches and inhabits sandy regions of the lower shore

102

105

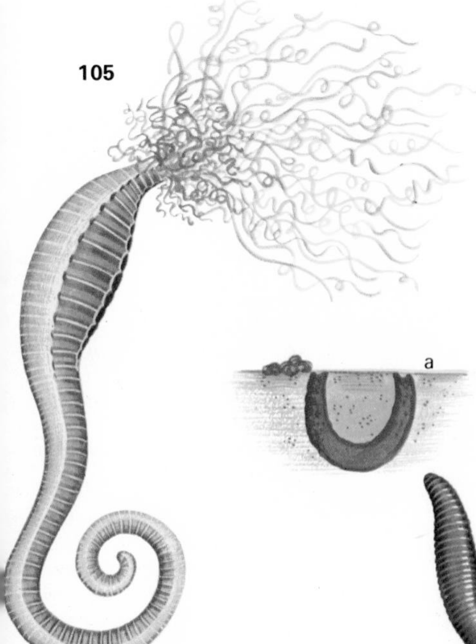

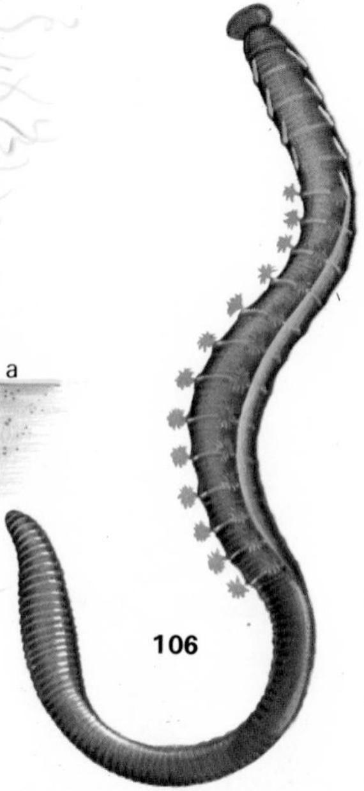

106

a

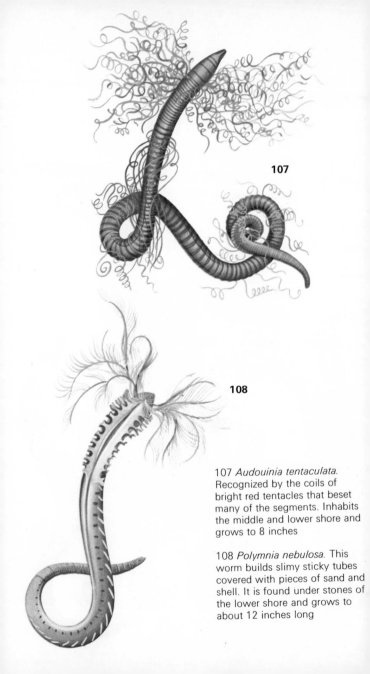

107

108

107 *Audouinia tentaculata*.
Recognized by the coils of
bright red tentacles that beset
many of the segments. Inhabits
the middle and lower shore and
grows to 8 inches

108 *Polymnia nebulosa*. This
worm builds slimy sticky tubes
covered with pieces of sand and
shell. It is found under stones of
the lower shore and grows to
about 12 inches long

109 *Spirobis borealis*. The small clockwise coiled tubes of this species measure only $\frac{3}{16}$ inch in diameter and often cover the fronds of *Fucus* and *Laminaria* or the surfaces of rocks and stones of the middle shore. When immersed the worm will only then extend its green tentacles

110 *Filograna implexa*. The tubes of this species reach 6 inches high and are usually confined to the lower shore where clumps are attached to pier piles and stones. The feathery tentacles, shown here at a high magnification, protrude from the tube ends

111 *Serpula vermicularis*. Although this species lives in sub-littoral waters, its tubes are often cast up on the shore. They measure 3–4 inches long and are frequently attached to the shells of *Pecten maximus*, Great Scallop

112 *Lanice conchilega*. The tubes of this species can reach 12 inches in length and are covered with small pieces of shell and sand. The species inhabits the lower shore

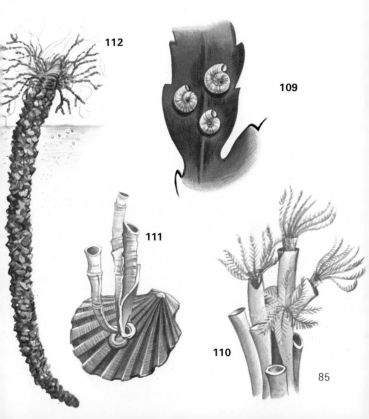

112

109

111

110

Marine Arthropods (Phylum Arthropoda)

The word 'arthropod' means 'jointed-legged' and the phylum includes a great number of animals varying widely in size and form. The largest most familiar class of arthropods are the Insecta. These, however, are very poorly represented on the shore below the splash zone and the predominant arthropod class of the shore is the Crustacea, that are represented by such diverse forms as barnacles, sea slaters, shrimps and crabs. Far less common are members of the class Pycnogonida, the Sea Spiders (page 108).

Class Crustacea

The body plan of the Lobster, *Homarus* will serve as an introduction to the chief features of the crustaceans. The common lobster varies in length from 8 to 20 inches and is blue in colour. It can be found among rocks but generally occurs off-shore. It is very widely distributed. The body is composed of a combined head and thorax (cephalothorax or carapace) and an abdomen of six articulating segments.

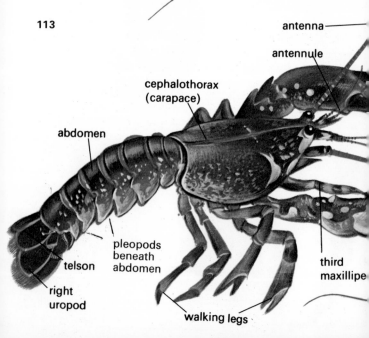

antenna

antennule

cephalothorax
(carapace)

abdomen

pleopods
beneath
abdomen

telson

right
uropod

walking legs

third
maxilliped

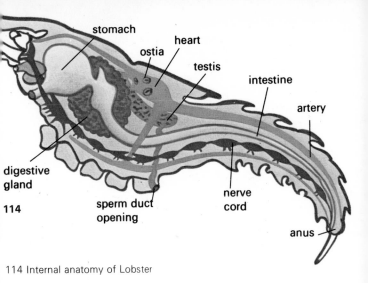

stomach

heart

ostia

testis

intestine

artery

digestive
gland

114

sperm duct
opening

nerve
cord

anus

114 Internal anatomy of Lobster

113 Body plan of the Lobster.
The paired appendages show
considerable modifications.
from one end of the body to the
other. The antennae and
antennules are sensory structures
and the following six appendages
are concerned with the sifting
and grinding of food particles.

nt
ela

The tearing of food is often
assisted by the claws (chelae)
as well as the two succeeding
pairs of walking legs that are
equipped with small pincers.
The first pair of the five
paired abdominal append-
ages, which are called pleopods, are small in the female
and the first two pairs are
greatly modified in the male
for the transferring of sperms
during mating. These paddle-
like pleopods, which are only
just visible in the figure,
assist the animal to swim and
serve, in the female, for the
attachment of eggs after they
are laid. The sixth pair of
appendages are modified as
uropods and together with
the telson form the 'tail fan'.

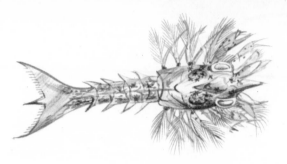

115 A zoeal planktonic stage of
Homarus, Lobster, (× 15)

Internally [114] the digestive system of the Lobster is
elaborated into three regions. The anterior and posterior ends
are lined with cuticle and, because they are ingrowths of the
exoskeleton (shell), they are shed when the animal moults.
It is the middle part that is elaborated into a stomach. The
forepart of the stomach chiefly stores food already shredded
by the mouthparts. Food is further reduced in size by the
grinding of the teeth (ossicles) in the middle stomach, called
the gastric mill. Only the smallest food particles can pass
into the posterior stomach as the food is screened by a
filtering mechanism. The finest particles can then pass into
the digestive glands that open into the posterior stomach.

An efficient respiratory system is provided by twenty
pairs of gills attached to the limb bases and body wall and
protected by the shield-like outgrowths of the carapace.
Arteries carry blood away from the heart as it contracts.
Blood flows from the arteries into the body spaces (sinuses)
and returns to the heart via the gills where it receives
oxygen. Blood enters the heart through minute slits in the
heart wall (ostia) as this organ relaxes. The Lobster's blood
is a watery-looking fluid tinged with blue. The respiratory
pigment that it contains is called haemocyanin, that functions
in a similar manner to the haemoglobin of other animals.

Although the Lobster is encased in a hard shell its body
tissue is constantly growing. Its body shell (exoskeleton)
cannot stretch to accommodate this slow growth and has

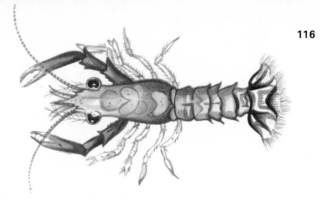

116 An early stage after settling
on the sea bed, $\frac{1}{2}$ inch

to be shed periodically. Such a process is called moulting
or ecdysis. An increase in size of its soft body occurs
immediately after ecdysis, chiefly through the uptake of
water.

When about to moult, the Lobster usually retreats into
hiding and the limbs and body are flexed periodically,
apparently in an attempt to loosen its old shell. Eventually
the body is bent so that a slit appears in the dorsal wall
of the carapace through which the anterior part of the animal
is withdrawn, followed by the abdomen. The withdrawal of
the limbs is probably the most hazardous part of this
operation and is facilitated by the longitudinal splitting of
the old skeleton in these regions. Sometimes, however,
a limb may break off during this process. After the Lobster
has emerged the skin becomes impregnated with lime salts
that harden it and the animal then assumes its normal
appearance and activity.

Eggs and sperms are ejected through minute pores on
the basal segments of the third pair of walking legs in the
female and on the fifth pair on the male. During mating,
packets of sperms are deposited near the female's pores and
the eggs are fertilized as they are extruded. Development
takes many months and the eggs remain attached to the
female's pleopods and are aerated and protected. The small
larvae, called zoeae, swim in the plankton and later settle
on the sea bed as miniature lobsters. The breaking off of

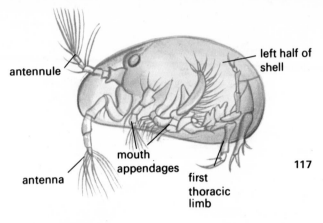

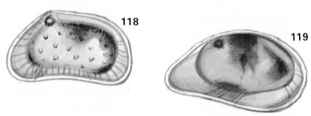

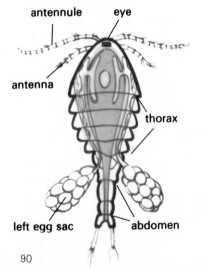

117 Structure of an ostracod

118 *Cythere lutea*, $\frac{1}{8}$ inch long

119 *Paradoxostoma variabile*, $\frac{1}{8}$ inch long

120 Structure of a copepod

90

limbs in larger crustaceans, although hazardous, is not uncommon. The Lobster, for example, will do this to escape from a predator. The phenomenon is called autotomy. The limb will usually break at a well-defined plane and the tissue will contract, preventing excessive loss of blood.

The commonest shore crustaceans are represented by four sub-classes. These are the Ostracoda, Copepoda, Cirrepedia, (barnacles), and Malacostraca, (sea slaters, shrimps, lobsters and crabs).

The carapace of an ostracod [117] is expanded into a bean-shaped shell, the two halves of which completely enclose the rest of the body. The limbs which are reduced in size, assisted by the antennules and antenna, are used for swimming. Ostracods are often found in rock-pools gliding over seaweeds. The two common species shown here are *Cythere lutea* and *Paradoxostoma variabile*.

The general structure of a copepod is shown in figure 120. The carapace is absent and the thoracic limbs, antennae and antennules assist to propel the animal through the water in a characteristically jerky manner. Females have egg sacs attached to the last thoracic somite. The eggs hatch as small larvae, called nauplii, that swim in the plankton. The two species [121, 122] are common inhabitants of rock pools.

121 *Acartia clausi*, $\frac{1}{16}$ inch

122 *Mesochra lilljeborgi*, $\frac{1}{16}$ inch

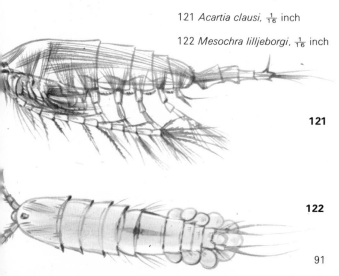

121

122

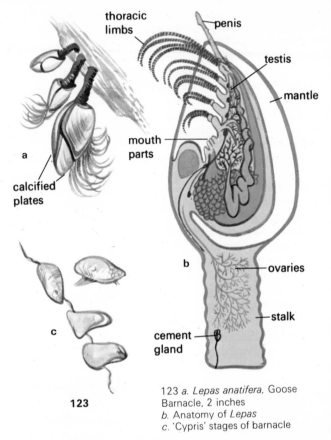

thoracic limbs

penis

testis

mantle

mouth parts

calcified plates

a

b

ovaries

stalk

c

cement gland

123 a. *Lepas anatifera*, Goose Barnacle, 2 inches
b. Anatomy of *Lepas*
c. 'Cypris' stages of barnacle

123

The barnacles (sub-class Cirripedia) are the most modified of all the free-living crustaceans. The Goose Barnacle, *Lepas anatifera* is shown in figure 123 *a* and its internal structure in *b*. The carapace (mantle) is composed of five calcified plates and the appendages are enclosed within the mantle cavity. The mouth parts are inconspicuous but the six pairs of thoracic limbs are well developed. When the plates are held apart the limbs can be seen combing the water for food particles. The stalk represents the head and the far end is cemented to a piece of drift wood or other object.

Barnacles are hermaphrodites but self-fertilization is probably not common as the prominent penis can transfer sperms to adjacent specimens. The eggs hatch as minute nauplii, each changing into a 'cypris-stage' as shown in figure 123 c, that soon settles on to a suitable substrate and develops into a young barnacle.

The Goose Barnacle is only occasionally found in the shore flotsam but the Acorn Barnacles are the most prolific shore-dwelling crustaceans. They are not stalked and firmly encrust all suitable surfaces exposed to wave action. *Balanus balanoides*, which has broad calcified 'rostral' plates, is common on the northern coasts while *Chthamalus stellatus* in which the rostral plates are narrow, occurs on the west and south-west coasts of the British Isles where it is very abundant.

Some cirripedes are parasitic on other crustaceans. The commonest of these is *Sacculina carcini* that is frequently seen as an oval mass attached to the abdomen of *Carcinus maenas* the Shore Crab.

124 Acorn Barnacle, *Balanus balanoides*, ½ inch high
125 *Chthamalus stellatus*, ½ inch tall
126 *Sacculina carcini* parasitizing *Carcinus*, Shore Crab, ¾ inch broad

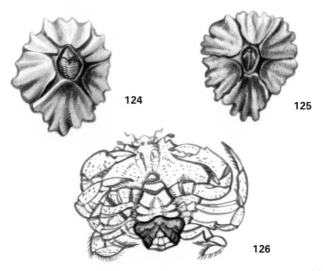

124

125

126

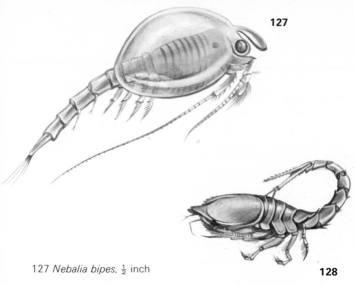

127 *Nebalia bipes,* $\frac{1}{2}$ inch

128 *Diastylis rathkii,* $\frac{1}{2}$ inch long

The sub-class Malacostraca contains many different forms. The super-order Leptostraca is represented on the shore by the small *Nebalia bipes* [127] that has a well developed carapace, stalked eyes, a prominent rostrum and thoracic limbs that are all of the same shape. *Nebalia* inhabits the regions of the middle and lower shore and is found under stones and seaweed where it is sometimes found in large numbers feeding on decaying fish.

The super-order Peracarida contains five orders all represented on the shore. All female peracaridans have a brood pouch formed by ingrowths of parts of the thorcic limbs in which the eggs are carried until they hatch, miniatures of their parents.

Members of the order Cumacea burrow into sand or muddy gravel and the largest shore species reaches about $\frac{1}{2}$ inch in length. A common species is *Diastylis rathkii* [128]. The inflated carapace bears a pair of small eyes set close together. The abdomen can be flexed to bring the uropods to within reach of most parts of the body where they clean detritus from the body surface or appendages.

The mysids, order Mysidacea, are abundant in oceanic waters and provide an important diet for fishes. The shore species rarely exceed 1 inch in length and are distinguished from the true shrimps (page 100) by their small pleopods and bifurcate legs, a feature that once endowed them with the name 'schizopoda' meaning 'split feet'. The thoracic legs provide their chief means of locomotion and respiration. Mysids, along with many shrimps, exhibit an 'escape mechanism' when disturbed. The animal rapidly bends and extends its abdomen. This causes water beneath it to become suddenly displaced and results in a powerful backward spring by the animal often projecting it some considerable distance. *Schistomysis spiritus* has a clear glassy body and prominent black eyes. It migrates towards the shore at night and is often left stranded in rock-pools. *Praunus neglectus* [130] is common on the lower shore among seaweed. This species is distinguished from *Praunus flexuosus*, Chaemaelon Prawn (a common inhabitant of estuaries and lagoons) by its grass-green colour that varies from dark olive to pale green.

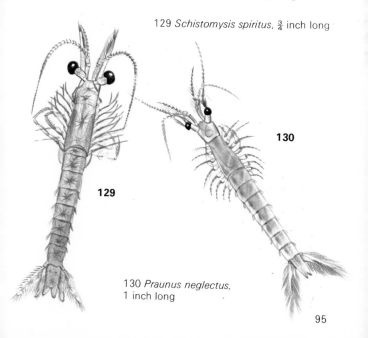

129 *Schistomysis spiritus*, ¾ inch long

130

129

130 *Praunus neglectus*,
1 inch long

The largest shore dwelling species of the order Isopoda is *Ligia oceanica* the Sea Slater growing to 1 inch in length and a close relative of the terrestrial woodlice. It occupies crevices of rocks and breakwaters of the upper shore and splash zone and is a nocturnal creature that at night will descend from hiding to feed upon the seaweed that forms the chief part of its diet in some localities. The female *Jaera albifrons*, [132] measures just over $\frac{1}{8}$ inch in length and the male [133] about $\frac{1}{16}$. It is common amongst algae, under stones and where fresh water runs over the shore. It often occurs in sheltered situations along with *Jaera nordmanii*, recognized by its more oval-shaped body and more setosed margins.

Sphaeroma serratum is a common species under rocks and in crevices of pier piles on the middle and lower shore and it often shows considerable variation in its colour pattern. This species can roll into a ball as shown in figure 135, a position that it usually assumes when out of water. Grows to $\frac{1}{2}$ inch in length. *Idotea granulosa* is a common isopod on many shores where it is often found among seaweeds such as *Ascophyllum* and *Fucus* (page 33). Its colour can vary according to the weed it inhabits and adult females reach $\frac{3}{4}$ inch in length. A smaller shore dwelling species is *Idotea pelagica*, recognized by its rounded telson and purple-brown colour broken by white stripes down the mid-line of the body. It is found on exposed shores especially where barnacles are abundant. *Limnoria lignorum*, the Gribble [137 a] measures just over $\frac{1}{8}$ inch in length and its presence is usually recognized by the numerous holes and burrows that it makes in jetties or pier piles. These small holes lead into tunnels that run parallel to, and just below, the surface of the wood [b]. The burrows end blind and through the holes water is drawn for respiratory purposes. Usually each tunnel will be occupied by a male and female *Limnoria*.

131 *Ligia oceanica*, Sea Slater, 1 inch long
132 *Jaera albifrons*, female, $\frac{1}{8}$ inch long
133 Male of *Jaera albifrons*, $\frac{1}{16}$ inch long

134 *Sphaeroma serratum*, $\frac{1}{2}$ inch
135 Same rolled into a ball
136 *Idotea granulosa*, $\frac{3}{4}$ inch
137 a. *Limnoria lignorum*, Gribble, $\frac{1}{8}$ inch
b. Wood bored by *Limnoria*

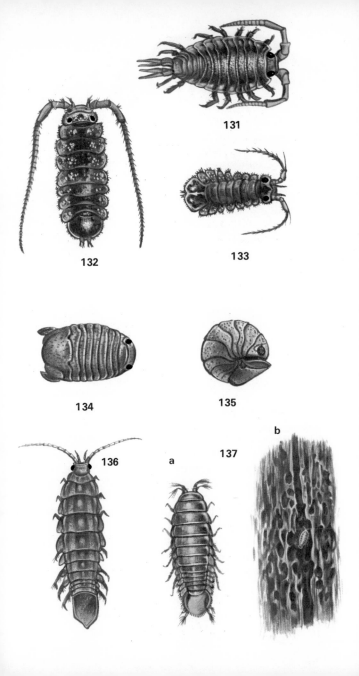

131

132

133

134

135

136

137 a b

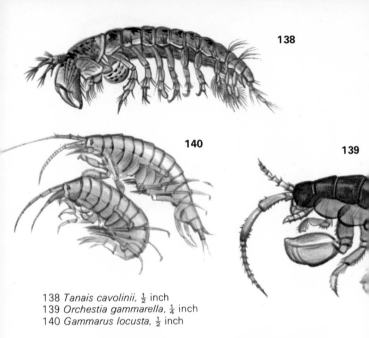

138 *Tanais cavolinii*, ½ inch
139 *Orchestia gammarella*, ¼ inch
140 *Gammarus locusta*, ½ inch

The boring is done by the female with her sharp jaws (mandibles) that work on a rasp and file principle and they are very effective in cutting the hard wood. When the young are released from the brood pouch they soon begin to burrow into the walls of the parent burrow and in this way much of the wood becomes permeated with holes. *Limnoria* is most active and abundant just above the sublittoral zone where the pier piles will often show a noticeable erosion due to their activity.

Only a few species of the order Tanaidacea occupy crevices in rocks and breakwaters of the lower shore. Shown here is *Tanais cavolinii* [138] distinguished by its small carapace and eyes on immovable processes.

Members of the order Amphipoda, are compressed from side to side unlike the isopods that are dorsally flattened. A large number of these individuals live between the tide marks, chiefly under stones and in the rotting seaweed at the top of the beach. Figure 139 depicts one of the many species of Beach Fleas or Sandhoppers, *Orchestia gammarella*,

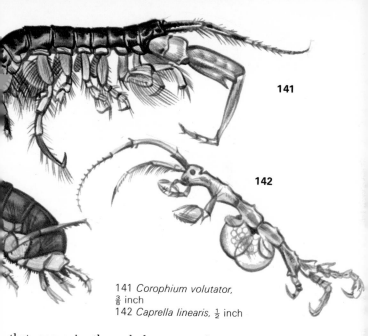

141 *Corophium volutator*, ⅜ inch
142 *Caprella linearis*, ½ inch

that occur in the splash zone and among the stranded vegetation on which they feed. They jump rapidly when disturbed, achieved by a rapid extension of the abdomen. Most amphipods harden their skin with deposits of calcium carbonate but this is absent in the sandhoppers and the skin (cuticle) is soft, flexible and light. This has probably helped them to evolve the jumping habit.

Gammarus locusta represents one of the many species of Scuds. It is about 1 inch in length and variably coloured, although it is typically a brownish-green. It is found under stones on the middle and lower shore. During the breeding season the male and female are often seen swimming attached to each other as shown in the figure. Some of the holes in the mud flats at low tide will be occupied by the burrowing *Corophium volutator* [141]. A female specimen shown here will carry eggs in the brood pouch. Among the branching hydroids (page 58) or the red seaweeds (page 35) is often found the small *Caprella linearis* Skeleton Shrimp whose body shape blends in well with its surroundings.

The super-order Eucarida includes the shrimps and crabs. In contrast to the peracaridans (page 94), the eggs that are carried by the female eucaridans are always attached to the pleopods and these eggs usually hatch as minute zoaea (larvae) that complete a series of changes (metamorphose) before assuming the shape of the adult. The shrimps have well-developed abdomens and pleopods and are very active swimmers. It is this habit that has given them the name of 'natant' crustaceans in contrast to the lobsters, hermit crabs and true crabs that have adopted a crawling habit and are therefore called 'reptant' forms. The Hermit Crabs, along with the Squat Lobsters and the Porcelain Crabs (page 102) have asymmetrical abdomens that, in the latter two forms, are carried tucked beneath the thorax. In contrast to these the Hermit Crabs have coiled abdomens that are concealed in gastropod shells (page 103). The abdomens of true crabs are reduced in size to oval or triangular flaps carried beneath the broad and prominent cephalothorax. All the reptant forms have well-developed walking legs that reach the greatest mobility in the crabs.

The lobster pots on the quay and the shrimp catchers pushing their large nets through the sub-littoral waters are often familiar sights of the seashore. Lobster pots are baited with pieces of fish before being laid in the off-shore waters. On the south coast of the British Isles shrimps are often

143 A Pandle net

144 A kype

caught in a large push net called a Pandle [143]. In other coastal waters stalked nets or basket-work traps that are called Kypes are used. These devices are fixed into the mud flats and the incoming tide sweeps the shrimps into the traps. They are then emptied by the fishermen as the tide ebbs. The catch will often comprise two common species *Crangon vulgaris*, the Brown Shrimp [145] and *Leander serratus*, the Common Prawn. The former species can be recognized by its dorsally compressed body and the latter by its saw-like rostrum. The shrimp can be found in places where there is sand, the Common Prawn in pools among the seaweed on the lower shore. Occasionally a prawn may be discovered with a swelling of one side of the carapace, usually more noticeable when the catch has been cooked. It is caused by a small isopod parasite, *Bopyrus squillarum*.

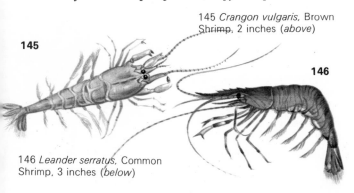

145 *Crangon vulgaris*, Brown Shrimp, 2 inches (*above*)

146 *Leander serratus*, Common Shrimp, 3 inches (*below*)

There are many species of reptant crustaceans that inhabit the rock pools of the mid and lower shore. Forms such as the Common Lobster [113] and the smaller Dublin Bay Prawn, or Norwegian Lobster, (*Nephrops norvegicus*) are not true shore inhabitants, although small specimens may be occasionally found in deep rock pools. Likewise small specimens of the Spiny Lobster or Crawfish (*Palinurus elephas*) are also sometimes found in shore pools. This latter animal, as its name implies, has its carapace and legs covered with hard and prominent spines. The Common Lobster and the Dublin Bay Prawn belong to the tribe Astacura and the Spiny Lobster to the tribe Palinura.

The three species of crustaceans depicted in figures 147 to 149 are representative of the tribe Anomura, some of which have asymmetrical abdomens. The smallest species likely to be encountered on the shore is *Porcellana platycheles*, Broad Clawed Porcelain Crab [147]. Its broad claws distinguish it from its close relative *Porcellana longicornis*, the Long Clawed Porcelain Crab. The flattened body of these crabs affords

147

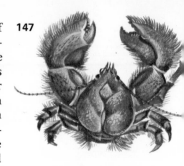

147 *Porcellana platycheles*, Broad-clawed Porcelain Crab, ½ inch

148

148 *Galathea squamifera*, a Squat Lobster, 2 inches

them some protection when pressed against the undersides of rock surfaces. Both species are fairly common on the south-west coasts of the British Isles. *Galathea squamifera* [148] is the most frequently encountered Squat Lobster, inhabiting rock pools and rock crevices of the lower shore.

The largest British Hermit Crab is *Pagurus bernhardus*, Common Hermit Crab [149], that occurs all round the British Isles. Small specimens are frequently found scrambling around in pools on the mid and lower shore. They always have their soft and vulnerable abdomens safely tucked into empty shells of the Dog Whelk (*Nucella lapillus*), or in other small gastropod shells. The spiral abdomen of the Hermit is well suited for fitting into the similarly curved shell of the mollusc, as it is held in place by modified uropods at the end of the abdomen. When the hermit retreats into the shell the larger of its two claws (usually the right) can conveniently block the entrance to the shell. As the crab grows, however, it is compelled to seek a larger shell and with this increasing size the Hermit usually migrates to deeper water and often chooses an empty shell

149 *Pagurus bernhardus*,
Common Hermit Crab, 3 inches

149

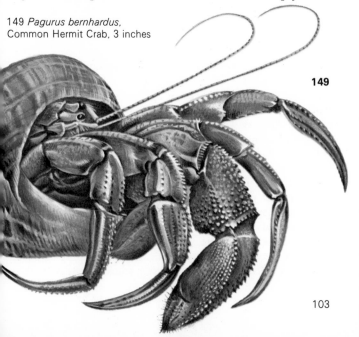

of the Common Whelk (*Buccinum undatum*). Each shell is usually explored carefully both inside and out before the Hermit finally chooses one to its liking and the change over from the old to the new shell is quite rapid as during the process the animal is vulnerable to predators. These large Hermit Crabs have often acquired a number of associates dwelling either on or inside the shell. Colonies of the hydrozoan, *Hydractinia echinata*, often cover the shell surface and in some localities the anemone, *Calliactis parasitica*, is often attached to the outside of the shell. It would appear to be advantageous for these coelenterates to be carried around, as the Hermit is constantly disturbing the many animals on the sea bed, some of which are caught by the anemone and hydroid. In return, the anemone affords the Hermit Crab some protection as any fish that attempts to attack it risks getting stung by the numerous thread cells in the anemone's tentacles. Often living within the shell occupied by the Hermit is the Ragworm, *Nereis fucata*, that will often extend its head when the Hermit is feeding in order to take food. A smaller species of Hermit Crab, *Pagurus prideauxi*, is far less common between tide marks but often carries the anemone *Adamsia palliata* on its shell.

The smallest of the true crabs (tribe Brachyura) of the shore is *Pinnotheres pisum*, the Pea Crab. The female of this species is always found living within the Common Mussel, *Mytilis edulis* [189] or the Horse Mussel, *Modiolus modiolus* [190]. Three common species of Spider Crabs of the shore are *Inachus dorsettensis*, Scorpion Spider Crab [151], *Macropodia rostrata*, Slender Legged Crab and *Maia squinado*, Spiny Spider Crab. The most frequently encountered crab, however, is *Carcinus maenas* [154], the Shore Crab or Green Crab. It is found in many habitats and can penetrate some distance into river estuaries. On some parts of the coast the crab appears to move into deeper water during the colder parts of the year. Some specimens will remain buried when the shore is uncovered at low tide while others are quite active. *Carcinus* is a true shore scavenger and is often a pest to fishermen because it will steal bait. It will also prey on some kinds of shellfishes such as *Mytilus*, whose shells it is very adept at opening.

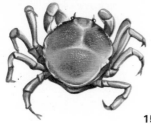

150 *Pinnotheres pisum*, Pea Crab, $\frac{1}{4}$ inch

150

151 *Inachus dorsettensis*, Scorpion Spider Crab, 1 inch broad

151

152 *Macropodia rostrata*, Slender Legged Spider Crab, $\frac{1}{2}$ inch

152

153

153 *Maia squinado*, Spiny Spider Crab, 6 inches broad

154 *Carcinus maenas,* Shore Crab, 4 inches

155 *Pilumnus hirtellus,* Hairy Crab, 1 inch

158 *Corystes cassivelaunus,* Masked Crab, 1 inch

154

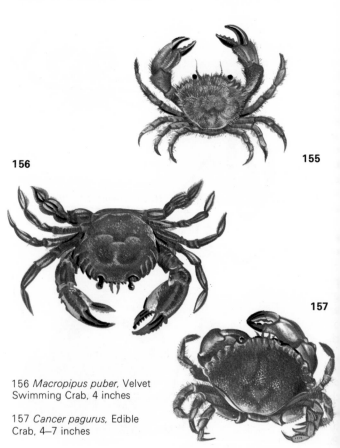

156

155

157

156 *Macropipus puber,* Velvet Swimming Crab, 4 inches

157 *Cancer pagurus,* Edible Crab, 4–7 inches

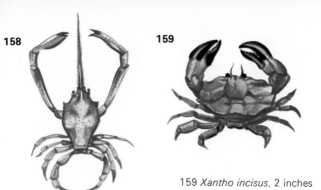

159 *Xantho incisus*, 2 inches

Mature male crabs can be identified by their triangular-shaped abdomens composed of five segments. The females have broad oval abdomens of seven segments. Both sexes can breed at less than a year old and mating is only accomplished just after the female has moulted and is still soft. Newly moulted crabs are called 'peelers'. It would seem that at least two batches of eggs can be fertilized from one mating and the eggs are often laid a considerable period, up to four months, after mating. Pairing and subsequent egg-laying continues throughout the year in British coastal waters and reaches its maximum intensity during the spring and summer.

Females carry their orange-coloured eggs attached to the abdominal pleopods and usually frequent the lower reaches of the shore until the eggs hatch, by which time they have changed to a grey colour. The zoeae [64 *d*] swim in the plankton and soon change to small megalopae, [64 *e*] that gradually descend to the bottom as they periodically moult and increase their size to become juvenile crabs. The colours of young specimens show greater variation than those of the adult. *Macropipus puber* or the Velvet Swimming Crab, [156] is very striking in colour and is an inhabitant of the lower shore. It is found along with small specimens of *Cancer pagurus* the Edible Crab. In contrast *Corystes cassivelaunus*, the Masked Crab [158] is a sand dweller. The tips of its long antennae, reaching upwards to the surface, form a respiratory tube. Two smaller Xanthid crabs of the lower shore are *Pilumnus hirtellus*, the Hairy Crab, and *Xantho incisus*.

Class Pycnogonida

The commonest species of pycnogonid, or Sea Spider, that is to be found on the shore, is *Pycnogonum littorale*. It can often be found attached to the outer surface of anemones and soft corals (pages 64 and 68) and it sucks the body fluids of its hosts. The male and female are sometimes found attached to each other and when the latter has laid her eggs they are carried by the male on a pair of appendages that are called ovigers.

The eggs of this Sea Spider hatch into small larval forms that are called protonymphs and these are equipped with rudimentary appendages. After several moults, however, these acquire the full complement of four pairs of appendages and fully developed mouthparts.

Class Insecta

Very few insects have become adapted to a true marine environment and they are essentially land-living creatures, although there are many species to be found just above the splash zone or among the decaying seaweed and flotsam of the upper shore. In this latter habitat is often seen the small dipterous fly *Coelopa frigida*, Seaweed Runner, and its relative *Coelopa pilipes* [161]. These flies are usually very apparent when the seaweed is disturbed, and at those times they will run rapidly over the weed and may even fly for short distances. The female deposits her eggs among the rotting weed and these hatch into small maggot-like larvae that soon change into pupae from which the adult fly emerges. In 1953 *Coelopa frigida* was so numerous on the south coast of England that their large numbers caused considerable annoyance to holiday-makers.

Of the numerous species of beetles, which belong to the order Coleoptera and are found under seaweed and stones of the upper shore and splash zone, *Aepus marinus* is very common [162]. A common primitive insect of the order Collembola that inhabits the surface film of rock pool water, especially where the pools are small and sheltered, is *Lipura maritima*. It measures about $\frac{1}{8}$ inch long and this species, along with other collembolids, is also found on rocks and weeds of the upper shore.

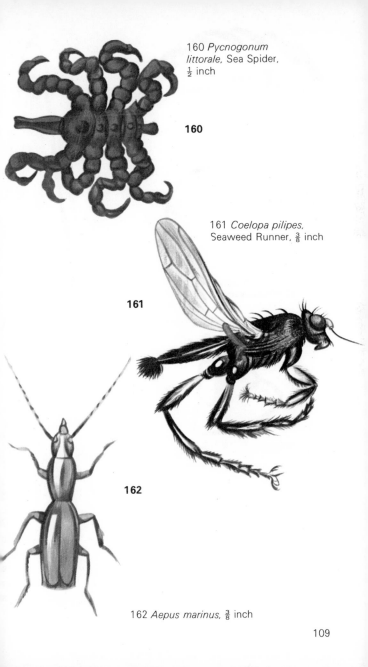

160 *Pycnogonum littorale*, Sea Spider, ½ inch

160

161 *Coelopa pilipes*, Seaweed Runner, ⅜ inch

161

162

162 *Aepus marinus*, ⅜ inch

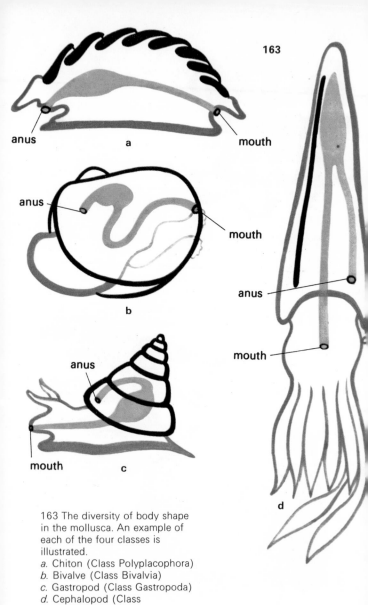

anus

mouth

a

anus

mouth

b

anus

mouth

c

anus

mouth

d

163 The diversity of body shape
in the mollusca. An example of
each of the four classes is
illustrated.
a. Chiton (Class Polyplacophora)
b. Bivalve (Class Bivalvia)
c. Gastropod (Class Gastropoda)
d. Cephalopod (Class
Cephalopoda)

Molluscans (Phylum Mollusca)

Next to the arthropods the phylum mollusca is the second largest group of the marine invertebrates. The word 'molluscus' means 'soft', and denotes the soft fleshy body of these animals that is often enclosed and protected by a hard shell. The flesh of many species is eaten by Man. The body plan of the mollusca show considerable variation in shape as shown in figure 163, *a–d*. These modifications of the shell (coloured black), alimentary canal (yellow) and foot (blue) contribute to the diversity of shape and habit in the phylum and have given rise to the four classes of mollusca, which are the Polyplacophora, the Gastropoda, the Bivalvia and the Cephalopoda.

Class Polyplacophora

The Chitons are the most primitive of all the shore-dwelling molluscs. They have a well-developed foot, are devoid of tentacles and their 'shell' is composed of eight articulating plates. Chitons are found firmly attached to the surface of large rocks or stones, from which they rasp off the small algae with the aid of their radulas [170]. Unlike the gastropods their organs have not been subject to torsion and the alimentary canal is a straight tube. Most chitons inhabit the lower shore and the two common species illustrated here are *Lepidochiton cinereus* and *Acanthochiton crinitus* [165].

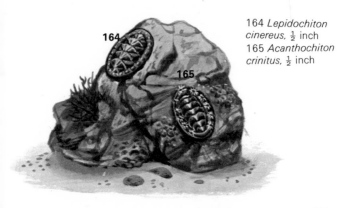

164 *Lepidochiton cinereus*, ½ inch
165 *Acanthochiton crinitus*, ½ inch

Class Gastropoda

The gastropods are the largest class of molluscs and the most varied in shape and habits. The structure of a gastropod is illustrated here by *Littorina littorea*, Common Periwinkle [166]. Here, the animal has been removed from its shell. The soft part of the body is composed of a prominent foot on which the animal moves. This is terminally capped with a horny operculum serving as a lid to the shell when the Periwinkle is withdrawn. The head carries a pair of tentacles, which feel and sense odours in the water. Each eye is placed at the tentacle base. The rest of the body, normally concealed by the shell is the visceral hump. The shell is a large coiled tube and the shape of the visceral hump closely follows the path of this twisting within the shell. Just visible when the animal is expanded is the mantle edge, that extends backwards into the shell, its walls enclose the mantle cavity in which many of the body organs, particularly the gill (ctenidium) is suspended. This gill is composed of triangular shaped leaves all richly supplied with blood vessels. The minute cilia that invest the surfaces of these drive a respiratory water current over the gill surface. The pigmented strip of tissue, the osphradium, is one of the Periwinkle's major sense organs and seems responsible for testing water as it enters the mantle cavity. Due to the rearrangement of the body organs during development (torsion) the alimentary canal has its posterior part placed above the head [163 c] and in the adult the anus is placed above the snout-shaped mouth.

Within the mouth is the buccal cavity containing a long ribbon of tissue, the radula, which is beset with recurved teeth [170]. The radula rasps off fragments of algae from rock

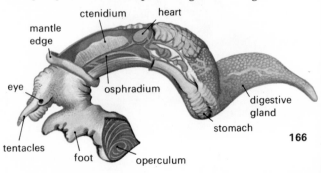

166

surfaces and these are conveyed backwards into the gut assisted by the lubricating saliva.

The heart is composed of two chambers and, although the periwinkle has a more elaborate system of blood vessels than the arthropods, the blood spaces or sinuses are still retained.

In *Littorina littorea* the sexes are separate. After pairing the females shed a number of egg-capsules into the water. Each of these contains up to five eggs. These capsules float below the sea surface and the eggs will hatch into minute larvae, each called a veliger [167]. The veliger is an active swimmer using the numerous cilia on its two large lobes (vellum). After about two weeks of this active mode of life the young developing periwinkle assumes its crawling posture [168] in preparation for its life on the sea bed.

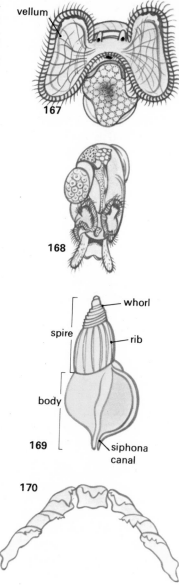

166 General features of a gastropod, *Littorina littorea*
167 Veliger of *Littorina littorea*, swimming stage, $\frac{1}{32}$ inch
168 Veliger in crawling posture
169 Structure and terminology of gastropod shell
170 A row of radula teeth of *Littorina littorea*

The class Gastropoda is divided into two sub-classes. The first is the sub-class Prosobranchia a representative of which is *Littorina*, that has already been described. Most prosobranchs have a shell large enough for the animal to withdraw into and the gill (ctenidium) is at the front end of the body and the head is seen to display only one pair of tentacles when the animal is crawling. This sub-class is again divided into three orders.

The sub-class Opisthobranchia is composed of the Sea Slugs and is the second sub-class of the class Gastropoda and contains animals in which the shell is reduced and fragile, or is absent. The gill processes are usually displayed at the posterior end of the body and two pairs of tentacles are present in the moving animal.

The Prosobranchia includes three orders. The first, the Archaeogastropoda, contains the Limpets and Topshells. Of all the shore-dwelling gastropods the Limpets are probably the molluscs most successfully adapted to the hazards of shore life. *Patella vulgata* the Common Limpet is very abundant on many shores, clinging firmly to rock surfaces and rarely being dislodged even by the strongest waves. The conical-shaped shell is well adapted to receiving the constant shock of wave movement and those limpets inhabiting exposed coasts have slightly taller shells than those living in sheltered regions. The eggs of the Limpet are shed into the plankton and the larval life lasts for about ten days after which the small limpet settles onto a rock surface. As the larger Limpets are females and the smaller specimens males it would appear that this mollusc changes its sex during the course of its life.

Besides *Patella* that can reach $2\frac{1}{2}$ inches in diameter, the small *Acmaea virginea*, White Tortoiseshell Limpet reaches only $\frac{1}{2}$ inch. It is not uncommon on the lower shore where it browses among the *Laminaria* fronds.

Only three species of Topshells are true shore dwellers, although the empty shells of others are washed up from the littoral zone. The commonest shore form is *Gibbula cineraria*. Grey Topshell or Silver Tommy [173], while the attractive *Calliostoma zizyphinum*, Painted Topshell [174] is to be found on the lower shore and in the sub-littoral waters.

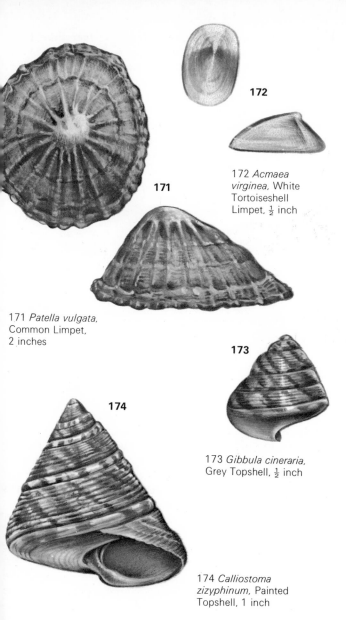

171

172

172 *Acmaea virginea*, White Tortoiseshell Limpet, ½ inch

171 *Patella vulgata*, Common Limpet, 2 inches

173

174

173 *Gibbula cineraria*, Grey Topshell, ½ inch

174 *Calliostoma zizyphinum*, Painted Topshell, 1 inch

The second order, Mesogastropoda, includes the Periwinkles, Spire Shells and Slipper Limpets. The habitats of the four species of Periwinkles found on the shore is governed by the ability of each to survive dessication. In the splash zone lives *Littorina neritoides*, the Small Periwinkle [175 *a*]. This species rasps away at the blue-green algae and lichens that grow above the high spring tides and, as its name suggests, it only reaches about $\frac{1}{8}$ inch in height. It can be found

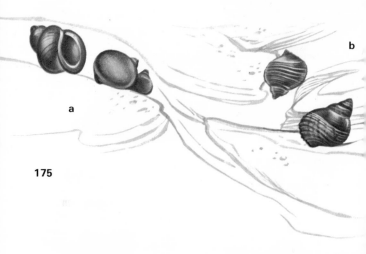

175

occupying crevices in rocks where it can occur in very large numbers. On the upper shore and higher parts of the middle shore occurs *Littorina saxalis* the Rough Periwinkle [*b*]. The shell of this species is rough to touch and grows to about $\frac{1}{2}$ inch high. It also varies considerably in colour, from black through dark red to an attractive yellow. This species prefers weed-free and exposed rock surfaces in contrast to *Littorina littoralis*. This is the Flat or Blunt Periwinkle [*c*] that reaches about $\frac{1}{2}$ inch and is confined to the middle shore and upper regions of the lower shore. It is usually found beneath the fronds of seaweeds. The species best adapted for shore life is *Littorina littorea* the Common Periwinkle [*d*] that reaches 1 inch high. It occurs on the middle and lower shore and can be found well into the sub-littoral zone. It is also very common in muddy estuaries.

Each of these four species shows interesting adaptions to its particular zone on the shore. *L. neritoides* and *L. saxalis* have reduced gills but the mantle lining is richly endowed with blood capillaries equipping these two species for true aerial respiration so that they are unable to withstand prolonged immersion in the sea. *L. littorea*, however, is not only well adapted for prolonged immersion, as it occupies the lowest regions of the shore, but can resist a considerable degree of drying when exposed. This is achieved by the extrusion of a layer of mucus from the glands in the foot that seal the lips of the shell to the surface of the rock and in

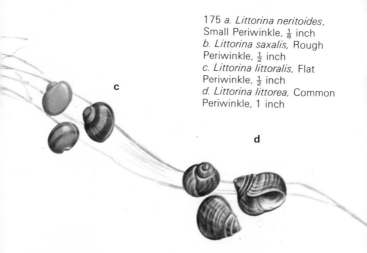

175 a. *Littorina neritoides*, Small Periwinkle, $\frac{1}{8}$ inch
b. *Littorina saxalis*, Rough Periwinkle, $\frac{1}{2}$ inch
c. *Littorina littoralis*, Flat Periwinkle, $\frac{1}{2}$ inch
d. *Littorina littorea*, Common Periwinkle, 1 inch

this way preventing any water loss from within the shell.

The breeding behaviour of *L. littorea* has been mentioned on page 113 but in *L. neritoides* the eggs are fertilized inside the body of the female and these are protected by an egg case when shed into the sea. These eggs are discharged only at one period in every fourteen days, coinciding with each spring tide and reproduction reaches its peak during the winter months. The female of *L. saxalis* retains the fertilized eggs that are born as young periwinkles.

Found in estuarine mud and often on salt marshes is the small *Hydrobia ulvae*, Laver or Spire Shell. This species is not easy to distinguish from *Hydrobia ventrosa*, which has seven whorls to the spire or from *Potamopyrgus jenkinsi*, Jenkin's Spire Shell that inhabits the higher regions of the estuary and often occurs in fresh water. This species has five and a half whorls to the spire.

The small *Trivia monacha* the Cowrie is a carnivorous species feeding on sea squirts (page 144). Although only $\frac{1}{4}$ inch long, its beauty is best seen through a hand lens. A mesogastropod introduced from American waters is *Crepidula fornicata* the Slipper Limpet [178]. Unlike the periwinkles it has no radula but the gills are specially enlarged to filter and trap minute food particles. The Slipper Limpet is a renowned pest of oyster beds where it smothers the oysters by its large numbers, as well as competing with them for food. The species lives in piles or chains, one animal resting upon another. The lowest specimens in the chain are the largest and are females while the smaller top specimens are males. Those in the middle of the chain are in the process of changing from male to female. This species is now very abundant along the south coast of the British Isles.

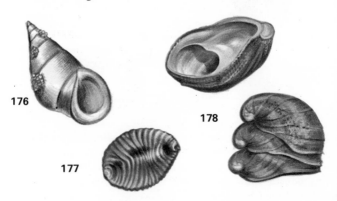

176 *Hydrobia ulvae*, Laver or Spire Shell, $\frac{3}{16}$ inch
177 *Trivia monacha*, Cowrie, $\frac{1}{2}$ inch
178 *Crepidula fornicata*, Slipper Limpet, $1\frac{1}{2}$ inches

179

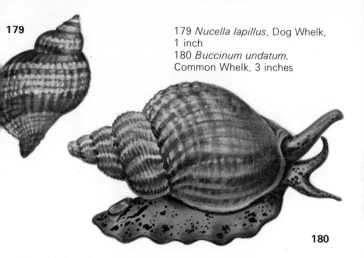

179 *Nucella lapillus*, Dog Whelk, 1 inch
180 *Buccinum undatum*, Common Whelk, 3 inches

180

The third order, Neogastropoda (Stenoglossa) contains the carnivorous Whelks. The two commonest species belonging to this order are *Nucella lapillus*, the Dog Whelk and *Buccinum undatum*, the Common Whelk. Both species are immediately identified from any of the mesogastropods described in having a soft tube (siphon) protruding from beneath the shell when the animal is extended. Through this siphon passes the respiratory water-current and this device can be held clear of the muddy substratum over which these molluscs often crawl. The radula of both species is thin, with well developed teeth, and can be extended as a proboscis. *Nucella* attaches itself to a Limpet and bores a small round hole in the shell through which it pushes its proboscis and rasps away at its victims flesh that is conveyed back into the Whelk's mouth. The Dog Whelk is also a prolific feeder on barnacles. The rostral plates of the barnacle are forced apart and the proboscis inserted. The colour of this Whelk's shell is variable and is influenced by its food. After pairing the eggs are laid in capsules each containing several hundred eggs, which are concealed in rock crevices. The young Dog Whelks hatch complete with shells and are swept from their position on the middle shore into the sub-littoral waters where they will feed on the polychaet worm, *Spirobis* [109] until they ascend to their place of origin again.

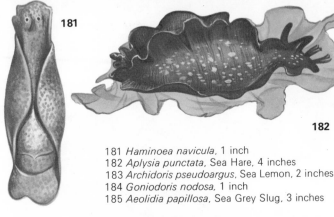

181 *Haminoea navicula*, 1 inch
182 *Aplysia punctata*, Sea Hare, 4 inches
183 *Archidoris pseudoargus*, Sea Lemon, 2 inches
184 *Goniodoris nodosa*, 1 inch
185 *Aeolidia papillosa*, Sea Grey Slug, 3 inches

The larger Common Whelk grows to 4 inches in length but only small living specimens are usually found on the shore. The egg capsules are large and empty ones are often washed up forming a common item among the stranded flotsam. *Buccinum* will eat dead as well as living molluscs. It will feed on oysters by waiting for the valves to open and then quickly slipping the edge of its own shell into the gap, thus holding the halves of the oyster's shell apart while it proceeds to rasp the flesh of its victim.

The sub-class Opisthobranchia contains the Sea Slugs which have lateral or posterior gills and have effected a considerable reduction of their shell size to a point where, in some species, it has been completely lost. They are extremely varied in their feeding and other habits but they are typically hermaphrodite creatures and a simplified classification recognizes two orders.

Slugs belonging to the order Tectibranchia have one large gill concealed in a cavity and the shell, because of its delicate appearance, is often called a 'bubble shell'. The fleshy outgrowths of the body (parapodia) are used for swimming. The two tectibranchs illustrated are [181] *Haminoea navicula* that inhabits muddy sand of sheltered bays and [182] *Aplysia punctata*, the Sea Hare. The shell of this species is reduced to a small plate covering the mantle. The Slug is sometimes found in large numbers browsing on the Sea Lettuce *Ulva*, that gives the animal its green colour.

183

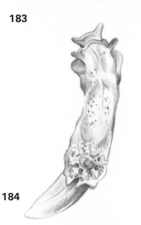

184

185

Young specimens feed on red seaweeds and are of a brownish hue.

The Sea Slugs included in the order Nudibranchiata are usually recognized by their foliaceous or cup-shaped processes that arise from the dorsal surface of the body and replace the true gills that have been lost. The shell is always absent. Three species are reasonably common on parts of the British coast. *Archidoris pseudoargus*, Sea Lemon [183], is often found feeding on hydroids and sponges. It breeds in the spring and its spawn is deposited on rock surfaces as inverted vase or cup-shaped spirals of some 2 inches in length.

Large specimens of *Goniodoris nodosa* inhabit rocky crevices or may conceal themselves beneath large stones where they congregate in large numbers. Reproduction reaches its peak in March and the spawn is deposited as a narrow belt containing numerous small eggs. *Aeolidia papillosa* is the Grey Sea Slug often found feeding upon sea anemones. It breeds during the summer months and the spawn is attached to rock sufaces as gelatinous cords.

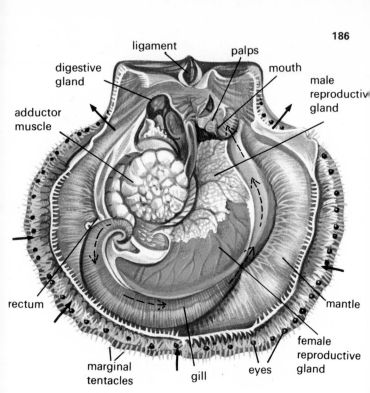

186 Structure of a bivalve, *Pecten maximus*

Class Bivalvia

The alternative names often used for this class are Pelecypoda meaning 'hatchet foot' or Lamellibranchia, meaning 'gill bearing'. Both terms are descriptive of the more obvious features of the bivalves. Forms belonging to this class are in many ways the most highly modified of all the molluscs, as the head and radula have completely disappeared and this has resulted in the evolution of a form of feeding known as ciliary feeding, described below for *Pecten*. An extreme development of gills has also occurred. Most bivalves are sedentary and many can firmly anchor themselves to the substratum while some can burrow using a well developed muscular foot. The bivalves have paired gills that hang in the mantle cavity and it is the cilia on these that create the powerful water current used in ciliary feeding. The ability to expel water from the mantle cavity is well developed in many bivalves as it has an important role in loosening sand, enabling the shell of burrowing species to penetrate this medium.

The body of *Pecten maximus* [186], the Great Scallop, is enclosed between the two halves of the shell. The top shell has been removed in this figure, but is normally hinged to the lower one by a shell ligament. Both halves of the shell can be drawn together and held tightly closed by the Scallop's powerful adductor muscle.

The Scallop has many sense organs but the most highly developed are the eyes. A hundred or more of these fringe the margin of the mantle along with the tentacles and are sensitive to light, although it is unlikely that they can perceive a clear image. The minute cilia on the large gill create water currents that bring food and oxygen-laden water into the body. This gill filters out food particles from the water, which are trapped in the copious gill mucus and carried towards the palps that filter out the larger and un-wanted particles. The remaining food is carried into the mouth. The broken arrows in the figure indicate the path of this food-current and the black arrows the water-currents.

The Scallop is an hermaphrodite and the reproductive bodies occupy a conspicuous position within the body. Spawning occurs from January until August reaching its peak in March. Unlike most bivalves the eggs are fertilized outside the body. These develop into larvae that eventually settle as miniatures of their parents. For a time the young Scallops remain anchored to the sea bed by the aid of their fine byssal threads. The Scallops and their relatives have developed an ingenious method of swimming by clapping together their valves. These can be opened to about 30° by a strong internal ligament and the powerful adductor muscle can close these valves very rapidly, which causes the expulsion of water. The direction of this expelled water is controlled by a thin membrane, the vellum, and this

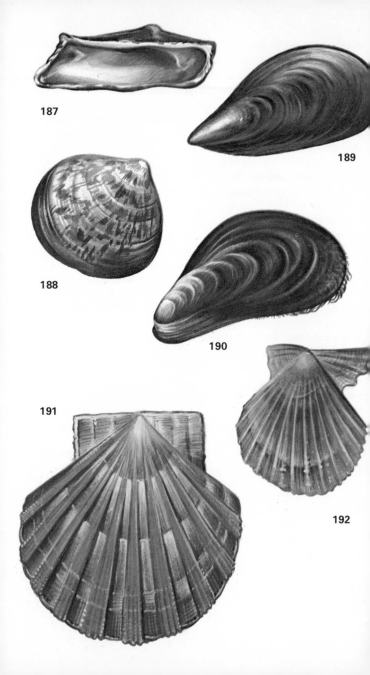

187

189

188

190

191

192

control allows swimming to be performed in at least two directions. It is often used as an escape mechanism.

Only a small selection of the numerous bivalves of the shore are illustrated in the following pages. Species such as *Arca tetragonum*, the Ark Shell [187] is often found firmly anchored to the substratum by its numerous byssal threads, a feature of many other bivalve molluscs. These threads are the result of a glandular secretion that hardens and the numerous filaments are strong enough to keep the mollusc anchored to a rock even in the strongest seas. Ark Shells usually inhabit the lower shore and are often encrusted with the tubes of serpulid polychaets.

Shells of *Glycymeris glycymeris*, Dog Cockle, are often washed up from the sub-littoral zone where this species lives. The most familiar and abundant bivalve is *Mytilus edulis*, the Common Mussel, which is often found growing in extensive beds from the middle shore downwards. Those inhabiting muddy estuaries have longer byssal threads that enable them to rise above the mud surface in order to draw in clean water. The chief predator of the mussel is the Common Starfish, *Asterias rubens* [223 *b*]. Sometimes within the confines of the mussel's shell is the small Pea Crab *Pinnotheres pisum* [150]. Mussels are extensively used as fish bait and large quantities are harvested for human consumption. A larger species of Mussel is *Modiolus modiolus* or the Horse Mussel, often found on the lower shore half buried in muddy gravel. The two species of Scallops illustrated here normally live in the sub-littoral waters but their shells are frequently washed up on to the beach. Figure 191 is *Pecten maximus*, Great Scallop and figure 192 *Chlamys* (*Aequipecten*) *opercularis*, the Queen Scallop.

Unlike the mussels, living Cockles are rarely evident on the shore as they live an inch or so below the sand surface. When covered by the sea they extrude an inhalant and

187 *Arca tetragonum,* Ark Shell, 1 inch
188 *Glycymeris glycymeris,* Dog Cockle, 2½ inches
189 *Mytilus edulis,* Common Mussel, 2 inches
190 *Modiolus modiolus,* Horse Mussel, 5 inches
191 *Pecten maximus,* Great Scallop, 4 inches
192 *Chlamys opercularis,* Queen Scallop, 3 inches

exhalant siphon that protrudes slightly above the surface of the sand.

Cerastoderma edule (formerly called *Cardium edule*), the Common Cockle spends most of its time buried an inch or so below the sand surface. The foot is well developed as a powerful organ for ploughing through the sand, and can make the animal move with considerable speed. This foot is also used to carry the Cockle along in a series of jumps, if the animal is washed up on to the sand surface. The foot is bent and then straightened suddenly throwing the Cockle upwards or along the sand surface. As a suspension feeder, the Cockle has an inhalent and exhalent siphon and when feeding the tips of these lie just above the sand surface. Cockles reproduce at a prodigeous rate and as many as half a million to the acre have been known to occupy large beds in the sandy regions in which they occur. A larger species, *C. aculeatum*, the Spiny Cockle, is found chiefly in the south west of the British Isles and extends well out into off-shore waters. In the time of Philip Gosse the sandy beaches at Torbay, Devon, were renowned for these large cockles, which occurred in great numbers. It was often called the 'Paignton Cockle'. The red colouring of the foot has also given it the name 'Red Nose'.

Acanthocardium echinata, Prickly Cockle, is less common than the former species and the shell ribs are beset with curved spines while *Dosina exoleta*, Rayed Artemis, inhabits the lower shore often in sandy bays. *Venerupis decussata*, the Cross Cut Carpet Shell [196] is found in the muddy gravel and sand of the lower shore where it is often abundant.

The best known of the British Wedge Shells is *Donax vittatus*, Banded or Purple Toothed Wedge Shell. It is found on exposed sandy shores living just below the sand surface. Also inhabiting the lower shore sand is *Gari (Gari) fervensis*, Faroe Sunset Shell [198].

The Tellins are recognized by having very compressed shell valves apparently leaving little room for their body between. This shape, assisted by their strong muscular foot, enables the Tellin to move rapidly through the sand. The commonest species are *Tellina tellina*, the Thin Tellin and *Tellina fabula*, the Bean Tellin [199].

193 *Cerastoderma edule,*
Common Cockle, 2 inches
194 *Acanthocardium echinata,*
Prickly Cockle, 2 inches
195 *Dosina exoleta,* Rayed
Artemis, 2 inches
196 *Venerupis decussata,*
Cross Cut Carpet Shell, 2 inches
197 *Donax vittatus,* Banded
Wedge Shell, 1 inch
198 *Gari (Gari) fervensis,* Faroe
Sunset Shell, 1½ inches
199 *Tellina fabula,* Bean Tellin,
¾ inch

200

200 *Macoma balthica,* Baltic Tellin, 1 inch

201

201 *Ensis arcuatus,* Razor Shell, 6 inches

Macoma balthica, the Baltic Tellin [200], is an inhabitant of sandy gravel, or mud, and is frequently found in the more sheltered regions of estuaries where its numbers can exceed 5,000 to the square yard. The shell has irregular striations, up to an inch long, and is more rounded in outline than the other species of Tellins. It is also less active and its tolerance of low salinities explains its occurrence in the Baltic, the feature from which it gets its specific name.

The bivalves best adapted to burrowing into sand are perhaps the Razor Shells of which *Ensis arcuatus* [201] is one of the common species. These molluscs have developed the technique of rapid burrowing to such a fine art that they are usually very difficult to dig out. Most species occur on the lower shore and are buried vertically with their siphons extending upwards. Only when the tide covers them do they move towards the surface and their siphons then extend and project into the water. As the tide ebbs, they sink down again into the sand. They appear very sensitive to slight vibrations and will sink at an amazing speed when disturbed. This movement is chiefly effected by the mobile pointed foot that is directed downwards into the sand. The foot can be expanded distally to make a firm anchor in the sand. As the foot contracts the rest of the body and the shell is pulled downwards. Rapid repetition of these movements enables the animal to move extremely quickly through the sand.

Mya arenaria, Common Sand Gaper, [202 *a*] is one of the largest of the British bivalves and a fully grown specimen can reach 6 inches in length. The siphon of this species can extend to twelve inches [202 *b*] when the animal is buried in the sand. This species occurs in large numbers in estuaries and can also live in brackish water. Only on a few parts of the coast is it collected for food and then it is known as a Clam. The Common Sand Gaper is, however, most commonly found in estuarine sand.

Some molluscs are very adept at boring into rock and wood, especially the Piddocks. These bivalves excavate holes in rock by scraping the surface with the minute, but highly efficient, teeth on the front ends of the shell valves. The valves are not hinged as in other bivalves and when

202

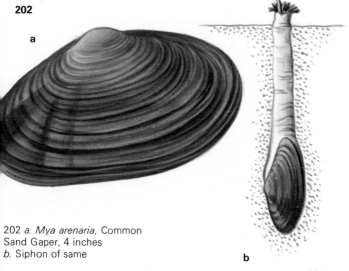

202 *a. Mya arenaria*, Common Sand Gaper, 4 inches
b. Siphon of same

203 *Barnea candida*, White Piddock, 3 inches
204 *Teredo navalis*, Shipworm, 6 inches
205 Piece of timber showing borings made by *Teredo*

the piddock grips the rock surface with its foot the valves
are pressed against the rock face and commence to scrape.
There are several species of rock-boring Piddocks, a common
species being *Barnea candida*, the White Piddock [203].

The Shipworms are wood-boring molluscs and are so
modified in their structure that they appear to bear little
resemblance to any members of this phylum. The bivalve
shell is reduced to two tiny valves situated at the front end
of the body and these are used as rasps for making burrows
in wood. In *Teredo navalis* [204] the body is elongate and
the small inhalant and exhalant siphons are situated at its
distal end protruding from the wood surface. The larva of
Teredo resembles the larvae of other bivalve molluscs but
as soon as it settles on to a piece of suitable wood the valves
quickly become modified into rasps and the mollusc soon
begins to bore a hole into the wood. The middle part of
the body lengthens as the worm penetrates further into the

wood. Pieces of timber bearing the borings of *Teredo* are sometimes found among the shore flotsam. Such a piece is shown in figure 205.

Class Cephalopoda

Many cephalopods have their shell embedded in the mantle tissue, where it is represented as a horny plate, or it may be absent. The foot may be composed of eight or ten tentacles. The more important anatomical features of a cephalopod are shown in figure 206. The mantle has been developed as a thick protective layer and is produced posteriorly into a pair of fins that steer the animal when swimming, as well as assisting its slower movements through the water. Cephalopods can move quickly by rapidly contracting the mantle cavity and expelling jets of water through the funnel. This funnel is flexible and can be turned to change the animal's direction of movement. The arms bear suckers that can seize food, often a live fish, that is drawn towards the mouth and quickly killed by the cephalopod's strong jaws. The gills are well developed and blood is pumped through the numerous capillaries by the gill hearts thus

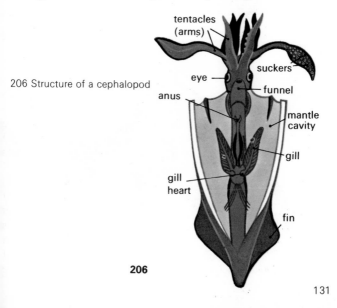

206 Structure of a cephalopod

206

207 *Sepia officinalis*, Common Cuttlefish, 12 inches

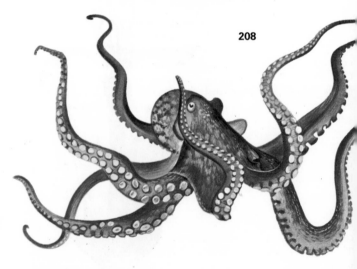

208 *Octopus vulgaris*, Common Octopus, 9 inches

209 Jumbo
210 Cockle Rake

209
210

keeping it richly supplied with oxygen. Cephalopods have a highly developed nervous system and the eyes are of a similar construction to those of a mammal. It is in this feature that they show a greater advance in development than any other invertebrate.

Although not strictly shore-dwelling molluscs they are sometimes found in sheltered bays and in pools during the summer months. Two species that may be found in such habitats are *Sepia officinalis* the Common Cuttlefish that belongs to the order Decapoda, as it has five pairs of tentacles, one pair of which is longer than the others, and *Octopus vulgaris*, Common Octopus [208] a member of the order Octopoda that has only four pairs of tentacles all of the same length.

Of the numerous species of intertidal molluscs undoubtedly the two most prolific species that are harvested by Man for culinary purposes are the Common Cockle [193] and the Common Mussel [189]. The former is an important item of the shellfish industries on the Lancashire and Welsh coasts and in the Thames Estuary where 'cockling' is a common sight on the shore at ebb tide. Cockles are collected by several methods. They may be raked out of the sand with a cockle rake or with a small bent pronged rake. In Lancashire a device called a 'jumber' or 'Jumbo' is used which compresses the sand and brings the cockles to the surface. Treading the sand has the same effect. The cockles are then washed and sieved and the smaller specimens are returned to the sea. After steaming, that kills and sterilizes them, the soft bodies can be separated easily from the shells by rocking in sieves. These are washed, packed in bags or pickled in salt and vinegar ready for sale. The shells are often ground into meal and used as poultry food.

133

Mussels are collected by a rake or 'labrake' in the deeper waters or cut off the rock surfaces with a sharp knife often made from a razor blade and corkscrew handle. Mussel beds are subject to sewage contamination and purification of the mussels is effected by allowing them to dwell in tanks of chlorinated sea water where their self-irrigation rids them of bacterial contamination. After successive washings they are suitable for market.

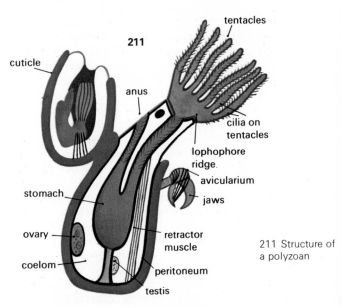

211

211 Structure of a polyzoan

Bryozoans (Phylum Polyzoa)

At first sight many bryozoans or polyzoans, as they are often called, can be mistaken for hydroids (page 58) or for pieces of dried seaweed. A close inspection with a hand-lens will soon reveal that nearly all members of this phylum are composed of many box-like compartments, each containing, when alive, a small polyp that, unlike the hydroids has its tentacles beset with numerous cilia. A diagrammatic section through two such compartments of a typical polyzoan is shown in figure 211. The specimen on the left is withdrawn into its hard case (cuticle) the one on the right is expanded. The tentacles are usually arranged on a horseshoe-shaped ridge or lophophore. The retractor muscles assist the polyp to extend and contract. There are no special sense organs but a single ganglion with nerves supplies the tentacles and intestine. Two forms of the animal (polymorphism) often occur in a single colony. The first is a vibracula form that has long cilia (vibraculae) that sweep backwards and forwards preventing settlement of suspended particles or small animals on to the colony. The second is an avicularia form recognized by its 'bird's head' structure, avicularium. The jaws of this device close on to any small animal crawling over the colony. The fluid filled body space (coelom) is lined with tissue (peritonium) from which the gonads arise. Bryozoans are hermaphrodite. Eggs and sperms are shed into the coelomic cavity and pass out of the body through a tube that specially appears for this purpose. Each fertilized egg can develop into a free-swimming cyphonautes larva that settles and grows into a new colony. Bryozoans are also able to reproduce by budding.

212

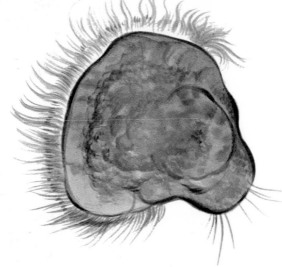

212 Cyphonautes larva of a polyzoan (× 500)

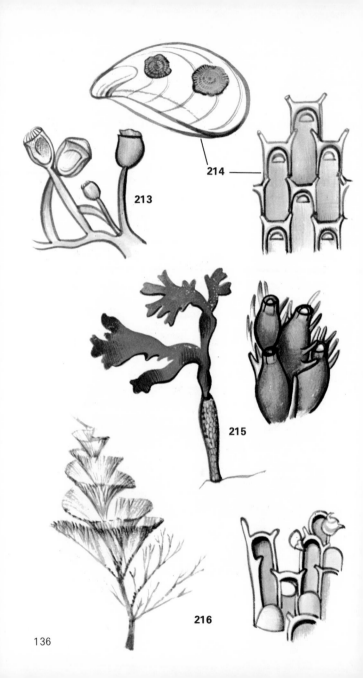

213

214

215

216

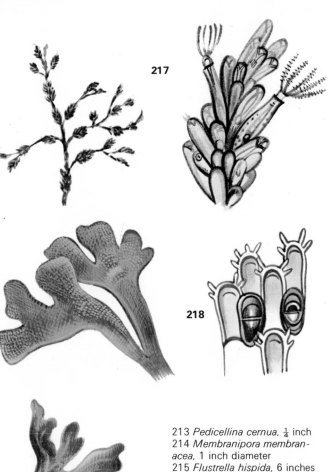

217

218

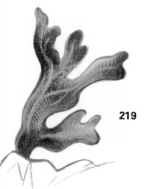

219

213 *Pedicellina cernua*, $\frac{1}{4}$ inch
214 *Membranipora membran-
acea*, 1 inch diameter
215 *Flustrella hispida*, 6 inches
216 *Bugula tubinata*, 1$\frac{1}{2}$ inches
217 *Bowerbankia imbricata*,
2 inches
218 *Flustra foliacea*, 4 inches
The insets to the right of figures
214–218 show the shapes of the
cell cases for each species and
at a high magnification (×30)
219 *Alcyonidium sp.*

The phylum Polyzoa was formally composed of two classes. The first, Endoprocta, is now a distinct phylum but for convenience is still regarded here as a class. A common species is *Pedicellina cernua* [213]. The second class is Ectoprocta. These may be encrusting species such as *Membranipora membranacea* that forms white patches on seaweeds, *Flustrella hispida* that forms grey patches on the Knotted Wrack and two branching species are *Bugula turbinata* and *Bowerbankia imbicata*. Frequently pieces of *Flustra foliacia* and *Alcyonidium spp* are cast up on to the beach from the sub-littoral waters.

Echinoderms (Phylum Echinodermata)

The echinoderms have evolved a body shape that is predominantly of a radial design in which many of the organs are so arranged that they radiate from a central point [220 *a*].

220 *a*. Structure of a Starfish *b*. Skin Gills
c. Pedicellaria *d*. Water vascular system

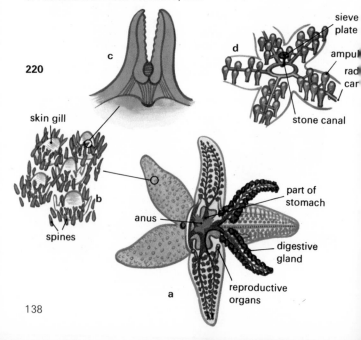

220

sieve plate
ampul
rad
car
stone canal
skin gill
spines
anus
part of stomach
digestive gland
reproductive organs
a
b
c
d

The body is soft but rigid. Support is provided by the numerous calcareous plates embedded in the skin. These have outgrowths of minute spines that project through the skin surface and which give the animal a spiny texture when it is handled. These spines also protect the skin gills that are the chief centres of respiration. Also guarding these delicate structures are the minute pedicellarias, pincer-shaped devices that can trap small organisms or debris that falls on to the body surface. An enlargement of a skin gill and its associated structure is depicted in figure 220 *b* and a single pedicellaria in *c*. The mouth of the Starfish lies on the underside of the central disc and the stomach is served with five pairs of digestive glands. The anus is small and there is no organized circulatory system and body materials are transported in the body spaces, forming a coelom, by the beating of minute cilia lining the coelomic walls.

The nervous system is simple and the principle sense organs are the eye spots, one situated at the tip of each arm and sensitive to chemical stimuli. The starfish moves by using a hydraulic pressure system called a water vascular system. The general structure of this is shown in figure 220 *d*. Water is drawn into the tubes through a minute sieve plate and finally reaches the ampullae via the stone and radial canals. When the ampullae contract, water is forced into the tube feet and backflow is prevented by the closure of a valve. The water pressure forces each tube foot to extend.

Each foot has a terminal sucker that can attach to a rock

221 Asteroidean larva (× 20)   222 Ophiuroidean larva (× 15)

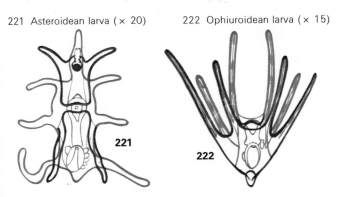

221   **222**

223 *a. Asterina gibbosa,* Cushion Star, 4 inches
b. Asterias rubens, Common Starfish, 6 inches
c. Starfish opening Clam
d. Palmipes membranaceus. 8 inches
e. Ophiothrix fragilis, Brittlestar, 12 inches

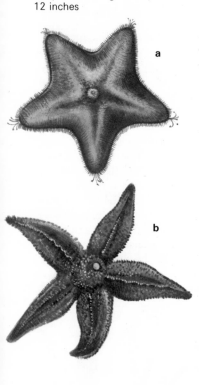

surface and if the longitudinal muscles of the feet contract the feet are shortened and the animal is pulled forward. The numerous feet working in unison enable the starfish to glide along at a fair speed. It is these feet that also assist in feeding. Starfishes are carnivores and can successfully open bivalve molluscs such as the Common Mussel. The starfish positions itself over the bivalve and applies the suckers of its numerous feet to both halves of the shell. A long and steady pull is exerted until the mollusc becomes fatigued and opens its shell. The starfish then everts its stomach pushing it into the gape in the shell and copious digestive juices then dissolve away the soft flesh. The sexes of the starfish are separate. A pair of ovaries or testes lie in each arm. Eggs and sperms are shed into the water and the fertilized eggs develop into small planktonic larvae. Two forms of these larvae are shown in figures 221 and 222. These have their body organs arranged in a

223

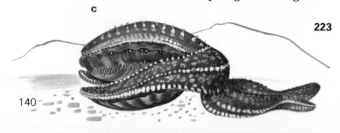

c

bilateral fashion and the radial body shape is acquired as the larvae metamorphose. Four of the five classes of the phylum Echinodermata are well represented on the shore.

Class Asteroidea
Species belonging to this class have no distinct division between the disc and the arms and the latter are usually blunt or short. The species illustrated here all have five arms. *Asterias rubens* is the Common Starfish or Cross Star [223 *b*] and can reach 20 inches in diameter although small specimens are usually found on the shore. It is a common species and a renowned predator of mussel and oyster beds. Reproduction reaches its peak during May and June and the larvae [221] are often very numerous in the plankton. The arms of the larvae have small sucking discs by which means they can attach to rock surfaces during metamorphosis. *Asterina gibbosa*, the Cushion Star [*a*] grows to about 4 inches in diameter and frequents the underside of stones and *Laminaria* beds where it feeds on molluscs and annelids. The eggs of this species are deposited in small groups attached to stones and development is direct as there is no free-swimming larval stage. It breeds from May until June. *Palmipes membranaceus* [*d*] reaches 8 inches in diameter and inhabits the lower shore and sub-littoral zone where it often lies buried in the sand. It feeds on crustaceans, molluscs and often on other echinoderms.

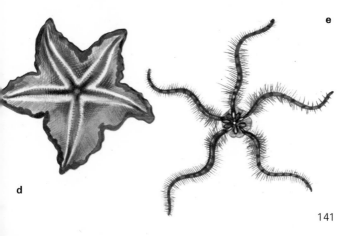

e

d

Class Ophiuroidea

In this class the species have a well defined disc and the arms are long and thin. *Ophiothrix fragilis*, the Brittlestar [e], grows to 12 inches and is abundant on the lower shore. The larvae [222] have long arms used for floating.

Class Echinoidea

Although at first sight the body shape of the forms belonging to this class seem to bear little resemblance to the starfishes, there are many similarities in structure, as shown in figure 224 of a typical Sea Urchin. The small calcareous plates have become greatly enlarged and are fused together to form a round shell that encloses and protects the soft body. The mouth is beset with a set of five teeth, radially arranged, that chew the food before it passes into the stomach for digestion. Two common echinoids are *Psammechinus miliaris*, a species that inhabits the lower shore among algae and stones and *Echinocardium cordatum*, the Sea Potato. [226] This species, as the former, grows to 2 inches in diameter and prefers sandy bottoms where it is often found in large numbers in burrows an inch or so below the surface of the sand.

A channel leads from the sand surface to the burrow, this latter excavation is lined with a secretion. The Sea Potato breeds throughout the summer when its larvae are often so numerous that they provide a substantial food item for many pelagic fishes. The small amphipod *Urothoe marina* lives as a commensal in the Urchin's burrow.

Class Holothuroidea

These are sausage-shaped echinoderms in which some of the tube feet are modified as tentacles. The calcareous plates are reduced to small spicules and there are no spines or pedicellarias.

Several species inhabit the British coasts and belonging to the genus *Cucumaria* is *Cucumaria frondosa* that grows to 18 inches in length and is sometimes found in large numbers on the lower shore in the *Laminaria* zone. The species illustrated here [227] is *Cucumaria normani* that reaches 7 inches in length and inhabits the south coast.

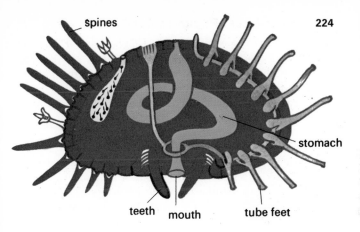

spines

224

stomach

teeth mouth tube feet

224 Structure of a Sea Urchin
225 *Psammechinus miliaris,*
2 inches

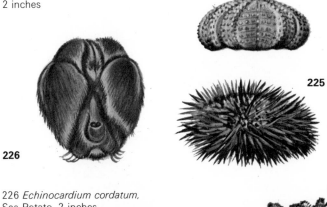

225

226

226 *Echinocardium cordatum,*
Sea Potato, 2 inches
227 *Cucumaria normani,* 7 inches

227

Protochordates (Phylum Chordata)

The chordates are animals with backbones and the more prolific and familiar members of this phylum are the fishes of the sub-littoral and littoral waters. There are, however, a number of primitive chordate forms belonging to the sub-phyla Urochordata and Hemichordata that inhabit the middle or lower shore.

Sub-phylum Urochordata (Tunicata)

The tunic wall of a typical urochordate is composed of a tough material resembling the cellulose of plant walls. This tunic encloses a sac-like body with two openings and it is through these that water is ejected with considerable force when the animal contracts, thus giving them the name of 'sea squirts'. The water entering the mouth carries food particles that are trapped in the mucus on the walls of the branchial chamber, a basket-like structure. The heart pumps blood first in one direction then the other. There are few blood vessels and the blood flows through spaces in the

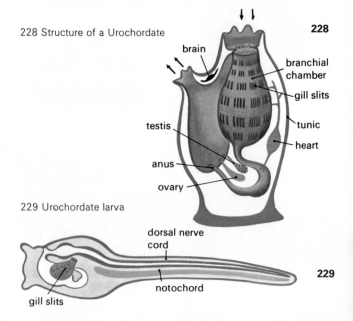

228 Structure of a Urochordate

228

brain
branchial chamber
gill slits
tunic
testis
heart
anus
ovary

229 Urochordate larva

dorsal nerve cord

229

gill slits
notochord

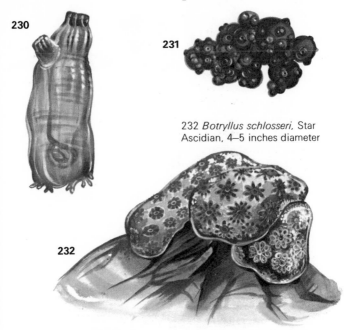

230 *Ciona intestinalis,* 5 inches

231 *Dendrodoa grossularia,* ½ inch

230

231

232 *Botryllus schlosseri,* Star Ascidian, 4–5 inches diameter

232

body tissue. The nerve cord and brain are simple. Urochordates are hermaphrodite animals. Eggs and sperms are shed into the water and a fertilized egg develops into a small tadpole-shaped larva [229] that possesses a well developed notochord (skeletal rod) and a dorsal tubular nerve cord, both important features of all chordate animals. The notochord is lost as the larva changes to the adult stage.

The three species of urochordates illustrated here belong to the class Ascidiacea. *Ciona intestinalis* is a solitary form reaching 5 inches in length and is common on the lower shore attached to pier piles. Individuals of *Dendrodoa grossularia* [231] are found living together with their basal parts fused to each other. They grow to ½ inch high. A common colonial species encrusting rocks is *Botryllus schlosseri,* the Star Ascidian [232], which has a jelly-like texture.

Sub-phylum Hemichordata (Enteropneusta)

The hemichordate *Saccoglossus cambrensis* or Acorn Worm [233] inhabits the sand and gravel of the middle and lower shore. The proboscis in some species is acorn-shaped and, assisted by the muscular collar is used for burrowing into the sand. The sexes are separate and the eggs develop into a small pelagic larva (tornaria) that in many features resembles the larvae of holothurian echinoderms. *Saccoglossus* is a fragile animal and will break up unless handled carefully.

Observing, Collecting and Preserving Seashore Animals and Plants

Marine aquaria

Many sea-shore creatures are seen at their best when alive, either in their natural surroundings or in some form of temporary receptacle. For prolonged observation an aquarium is desirable, but whatever type is used it should be of a rectangular shape and measure not less than $24 \times 12 \times 12$ inches in size. Smaller aquaria tend to be subject to greater and more frequent changes in temperature and are often more difficult to maintain than larger ones. Clear all-glass types will not be affected by the corrosive action of sea water but it is usually difficult to get one with optically clear glass. Metal frame types of stainless steel are preferable to angle iron. Whatever type of aquarium is chosen it should be thoroughly cleaned and allowed to stand full of water for at least a week before being put into use.

A marine aquarium should be filled to only half its capacity. This gives a greater surface to volume ratio that assists in the aeration of the water. Supplies of clean sea-water are usually a problem for those living far inland but it can be purchased in quantity from the Director of the Plymouth Marine Laboratory, at Plymouth, to whom enquiries should be sent. Sea-water collected from the sub-littoral zone is suitable for the aquarium, providing certain precautions are taken. It should not be collected near a sewage outfall and must be filtered and allowed to stand a few days before use. Successful marine aquaria have been maintained using part natural and part artificial sea-water. A well tried formula for the latter is: $46\frac{1}{2}$ oz. kitchen block salt, $3\frac{1}{2}$ oz. magnesium sulphate, $5\frac{1}{4}$ oz. magnesium chloride and 2 oz. potassium sulphate to $13\frac{1}{4}$ gallons of tap water. Tidmann's Sea Salt, obtained from a pharmaceutical chemist, is also a good substitute when it is dissolved in distilled water to bring the specific gravity to around 1.026. The salinity of aquarium water is important for although many shore animals can tolerate low salinities few will live

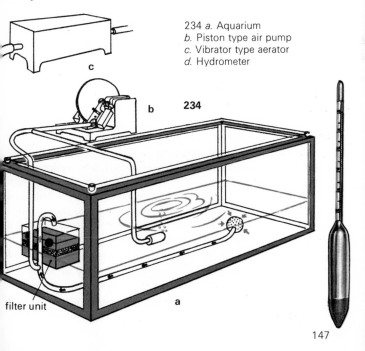

234 a. Aquarium
b. Piston type air pump
c. Vibrator type aerator
d. Hydrometer

234

filter unit

in water of a higher salinity than normal sea-water. Fortunately the specific gravity of sea-water gives a fairly accurate measurement of its salinity. Normal sea-water gives a hydrometer reading of 1.026. It must be remembered that as the aquarium-water evaporates its salt content will increase. Only distilled water must be used to restore the water to its original level and the specific gravity should be checked regularly with a hydrometer [234 d]. A mark can be made on the aquarium glass to show normal water level and this should not be allowed to fall appreciably.

Rocks and sand collected from the animals' habitats can cover the bottom of the aquarium. The best types of rocks are hard sandstone, granite or slate as these do not readily dissolve in water. Too many crannies should be avoided so that dead animals are not hidden from view. Excessive daylight must be prevented from reaching the aquarium and if some form of illumination is required, a fluorescent tube is preferable to a normal tungsten bulb. The temperature of the water must not rise above 60° F or fall below 40° F and a satisfactory temperature for most marine forms is between 50–55° F.

Some form of aeration and filtration is essential. The type of apparatus shown in figure 234 a and b works very well in a small aquarium and is relatively inexpensive. The filter unit is filled with glass wool and granulated charcoal, or a proprietary brand of filtrant obtained from an aquaria dealer. A piston type air pump [b] is more reliable than the vibrator type [c]. The air pump should be kept above the water level to prevent siphoning back if the pump stops. Although shore animals are subject to tidal rhythms it is not necessary to provide tidal conditions in the aquarium as most forms will quickly adapt to conditions of captivity. This rhythm however will often be evident in some forms, such as the Rough Periwinkle [175 b] that will show activity at the time of high spring tides.

Sea-water is normally alkaline and gives a pH reading of 8.4 (pH is a quantitative expression for acidity or alkalinity of a solution). The alkalinity should be checked from time to time especially after setting up the aquarium and for the first week or so. A satisfactory method of determining the

pH is with a book of indicator papers that give the necessary ranges of pH readings. A strip of the paper is dipped into the water and its colour compared with the chart provided [235]. A noticeable fall in pH can mean for example, that more aeration is needed to remove excessive carbon dioxide or that a little chalk should be added to replace some of the carbonates removed by aquarium inmates.

Most marine plants are not suitable for inclusion in the aquarium as they will gradually deteriorate and foul the water. The hardiest invertebrates such as barnacles, shore crabs, periwinkles and some anemones can be maintained in captivity for long periods. Only a few specimens should be kept at any one time. It is not advisable to keep small and large active animals in the same aquarium, for example large shore crabs will soon eat their smaller brothers. Anemones, crabs and shrimps can be fed small pieces of cooked meat but residual food must be removed from the aquarium before it decays.

235 A book of indicator papers for testing pH of water
236 Method of feeding aquarium inmates

235

236

pH
7·0
7·3
7·6
7·9
8·2
8·5

Collecting

Animals and plants should be collected with a definite purpose in mind such as the compilation of a local fauna list. This requires careful collecting and proper preservation of the specimens for identification. Collecting can only be done successfully at low tide. Always consult a tide table before embarking on an expedition to the shore and if the tide is followed out the more active forms can be spotted and collected before they conceal themselves beneath rocks and seaweeds.

A wide-mouth thermos flask [237 *a*] is very useful for transporting live animals. A few ice cubes in plastic bags will keep the temperature low if placed in the flask beforehand. A pair of stout wellington boots is preferable to other forms of footwear especially on muddy shores. A stout

237

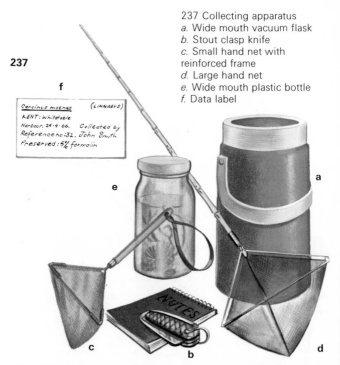

237 Collecting apparatus
a. Wide mouth vacuum flask
b. Stout clasp knife
c. Small hand net with reinforced frame
d. Large hand net
e. Wide mouth plastic bottle
f. Data label

Carcinus maenas (LINNAEUS)
KENT: Whitstable
Harbour. 25.4.66. Collected by
Reference no.31. John Smith
Preserved: 5% formalin

white metal bowl will withstand the effects of a shore breeze better than a light plastic type and is used for washing out animals from seaweed and later for anaesthetising them. A stout knife [b] is useful for prising off chitons or limpets from rock faces and for cutting free holdfasts of seaweeds, while a small hand net [c], with a stout frame and muslin bag, is used for sweeping under crevices of rock pools, and a larger one [d] for pushing over the sea bed in the sub-littoral zone. For the muddy shore a stout spade is necessary for digging up the burrowing forms. Finally, a selection of polythene bags and screw cap plastic jars [e] are required for transporting the collection home.

Preserving

Animals chosen for preservation should be undamaged and mature. They are placed in a bowl containing enough sea-water to allow them to expand fully. A 5% solution of formalin is added to the water, drop by drop, until the animals are anaesthetised and no longer respond to touch. 5% formalin is made by adding one part of commercial formaldehyde to 19 parts sea-water. Commercial formaldehyde can be purchased from a dispensing chemist. It is a poison and in an undiluted form its fumes will cause irritation to the eyes and nose. It must be kept in a well stoppered bottle and clearly labelled. When the animals are fully anaesthetised they can be carefully picked out and placed in a clean solution of 5% formalin that will fix (render their body tissues chemically stable) and also preserve them. Alcohol can also be used for anaesthetising fixing and preserving. However, only industrial methylated spirit or isopropyl alcohol is miscible with sea-water and this is usually available only to schools and institutions in quantity. Surgical and lamp methylated spirits are not suitable for preserving marine animals.

Before the collection is closely studied it can be washed and examined in tap water and returned to the preservative later. Provisional labelling of each sample done on the shore should now be elaborated into the type of label shown in figure 237 f. These permanent labels should be of a good quality rag paper and can be written with a soft pencil or in Indian ink. If the latter is used allow the label to dry and rinse in tap water before inserting into jar. Labels can also be affixed with a rubber solution or double-sided Sellotape to the outside of the jar.

Only hard shell animals such as molluscs, small crabs and the shore insects can be satisfactorily preserved in a dry state. Shells are usually kept in small cardboard boxes (match boxes are very suitable) and they can also be stuck on to pieces of white card and suitably labelled. Insects require more elaborate treatment as outlined in reference 45.

Plants are more easy to collect and preserve. They can be transported from the shore in polythene bags containing a little sea-water to keep them moist. Stages in the method for making a permanent herbarium preparation are shown in figure 238. Each specimen should be arranged in a dish containing a small amount of water and over a piece of

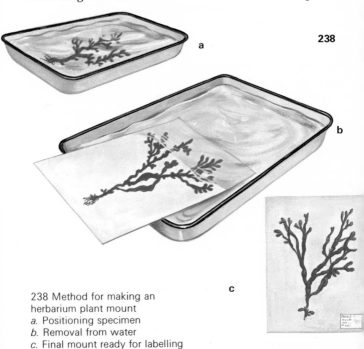

238

a

b

c

238 Method for making an herbarium plant mount
a. Positioning specimen
b. Removal from water
c. Final mount ready for labelling

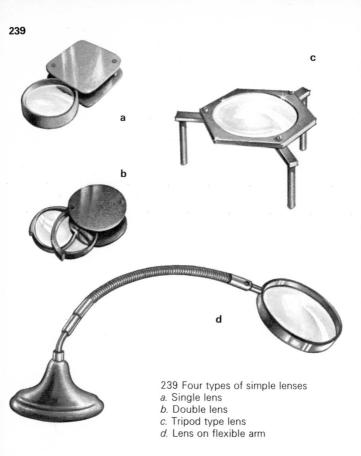

239 Four types of simple lenses
a. Single lens
b. Double lens
c. Tripod type lens
d. Lens on flexible arm

cartridge paper [a]. The paper and plant can be removed by sliding them out of the dish as shown in [b]. It must be covered with a piece of muslin and placed between several thicknesses of white blotting paper and several folds of newspaper and dried slowly under a light weight. The plant will often adhere to the cartridge paper but if necessary small strips of gummed paper can be used to hold the fronds in place as shown in [c]. These herbarium mounts can be labelled in a soft pencil or a small label can be stuck on to the back of the sheet. The mounts should be stored flat.

Identification, Nomenclature and Information Sources

Identification

In order to identify the animals and plants collected it will be necessary to examine them for the relevant features described and illustrated in the various monographs and papers listed on pages 154 to 157. In particular references 46, 48 and 49 should be studied carefully before identification is attempted. Many features can be seen with the unaided eye but a hand lens will be required for examining some forms. Four useful types of lenses are shown in figure 239, *a–d*.

Nomenclature

When a specimen has been identified it is then necessary to appropriate to it a scientific name. For example, the Flat Periwinkle (page 117) is labelled *Littorina littoralis* (Linnaeus). The first word denotes the name of the genus to which the specimen belongs (*Littorina*) and is the generic name. The second word *littoralis* is the specific or trivial name and serves to distinguish the Flat Periwinkle from its relative the Small Periwinkle, *Littorina littorea*. The word that sometimes follows the trivial name is that of the naturalist or scientist, called the author, who first used the name in describing the species.

Information

The following list of references will serve to introduce the reader to more detailed and authorative sources of information, particularly about the various animals and plants mentioned in this book.

MARINE BIOLOGY
1. Gosse, E. (1907) *Father and Son*, Heinemann.
2. Russell, E. S. and Yonge, C. M. (1963) *The Seas,* Warne & Co.,

SHAPING OF THE COASTLINE
3. Steers, J. A. (1964) *The Coastline of England and Wales*, Cambridge University Press.

THE TIDES

4. Pilkington R. (1957) *The Ways of the Sea*, Routledge & Kegan Paul.

5. Admiralty Tide Tables. *Vol. I European Waters*, Hydrographic Department, Admiralty.

PLANTS OF THE SEASHORE

6. Chapman, V. J. (1950) *Seaweeds and their Uses*, Methuen & Co.

7. Dickinson, C. I. (1963) *British Seaweeds*, Kew Series, Eyre & Spottiswood.

PLANKTON

8. Fraser, J. (1962) *Nature Adrift: The story of Marine Plankton*, Foulis & Co.

9. Hardy, A. (1958) *The Open Sea: Its Natural History*, Part 1, The World of Plankton, New Naturalist Series no. 34, Collins.

PHYLUM PORIFERA

10. Burton, M (1965) *Sponges*, Animals, 7; 436–440 and 456–460.

11. Bowerbank, J. S. (1864, 1866, 1874, 1882) *A Monograph of the British Spongiadae*, 4 vols. Ray Society London.

PHYLUM CNIDARIA

12. Allman, G. J. (1871–1872) *A monograph of the Gymnoblastic or Tubularian Hydroids*, 2 vols. Ray Society, London.

13. Stephenson, T. A. (1928, 1935) *British Sea Anemones*, 2 vols. Ray Society, London.

PHYLUM CTENOPHORA

14. Lilley, R. (1958) *Zooplankton Sheet No. 82* (see ref no. 47).

PHYLUM PLATYHELMINTHES

15. Wilhelmi, J. (1909) *Tricladen*, Fauna und Flora des Golfes von Neapel, 32.

16. Lang, A. (1884) *Die Polycladen (Seeplanarien) des Golfes von Neapel*, Fauna und Flora des Golfes von Neapel, 11.

PHYLUM NEMERTINEA

17. McIntosh, W. C. (1873) *Monograph of British Annelids*, Vol. 1. Ray Society, London.

PHYLUM ASCHELMINTHES

18. Southern, R. (1914) *Nemathelmia, Kinorhyncha and Chaetognatha*, Proceedings of the Royal Irish Academy, 31.

19. Coles, J. W. (1965) *A critical review of the Marine Nematode genus Euchromadora de Man, 1886*, Bulletin of the British Museum (Natural History, Zoology), 12 (5); 157–194.

PHYLUM ANNELIDA

20. McIntosh, W. C. (1908–1923) *Monograph of the British Annelids,* 3 vols. Ray Society, London.
21. Fauvel, P. (1923, 1927) *Polychètes Errantes* (1923) and *Sédentaires* (1927), Faune de France 5 and 16.
22. Muus, B. J. (1953) *Zooplankton Sheet No. 52* (see ref no. 47).
23. Hannerz, L. (1961) *Zooplankton Sheet No. 91* (see ref no. 47).

PHYLUM ARTHROPODA

24. Sars, G. O. (1922–1928) *An Account of the Crustacea of Norway, Ostracoda,* Vol. 9 Bergen Museum.
25. Sars, G. O. (1901–1921) *An Account of the Crustacea of Norway, Copepoda,* Vol. 4–7 Bergen Museum.
26. Wilson, C. B. (1932) *Keys to the sub-orders and genera of Copepoda,* Bulletin of the United States National Museum, 158 (Appendix B); 538–623.
27. Jones, N. S. (1957) *Zooplankton Sheets Nos. 71–76 (Cumacea)* (see ref no. 47).
28. Tattersall, W. M. and O. S. (1951) *The British Mysidacea,* Ray Society, London.
29. Naylor, E. (1957) *Zooplankton Sheets Nos. 77–78 (Isopoda)* (see ref no. 47).
30. Omer-Cooper, J. and Rawson, J. H. (1934) *Notes on British Sphaeromatidae, Isopoda,* Report of the Dove Marine Laboratory, (3) 2; 22–48.
31. Chevreux, E. and Fage, L. (1925) *Amphipodes,* Faune de France 9.
32. Allen, J. A. (1967) *Crustacea, Euphausiacea and Decapoda, with an illustrated key to the British species,* Fauna of the Clyde Sea Area, Scottish Marine Biological Association, Millport.
33. Bouvier, E. L. (1923) *Pycnogonides,* Faune de France 7.
34. Crowson, R. A. (1956) *Introduction and keys to families No. 4 (I).* Handbooks for the identification of British Insects, Royal Entomological Society of London.
35. Elwes, E. V. (1915) *Life History of a Shore Fly,* Journal Torquay Natural History Society 11 1; 3–7.
36. Fowler, W. W. (1886–1891) *The Coleoptera of the British Isles.* 5 vols. Reeve, London.

PHYLUM MOLLUSCA

37. Street, P. (1961) *Shell life on the Seashore,* Fabre.
38. Mathews, G. (1953) *A key for use in the Identification of British Chitons,* Proceedings of the Malacological Society, London, 29; 241–248.
39. Fretter, V. & Graham, A. (1962) *British Prosobranch Molluscs,* Ray Society, London.

40. Alder, J. & Hancock, A. (1844–1855) *British Nudibranchiate Mollusca*, 7 parts, Ray Society, London.
41. Tebble, N. (1966) *British Bivalve Shells. A Handbook for Identification*, British Museum (Natural History), London.

PHYLUM POLYZOA
42. Ryland, J. S. (1962) *Biology and Identification of Intertidal Polyzoa*, Field Studies 1 (4).

PHYLUM ECHINODERMATA
43. Mortensen, Th. (1927) *Handbook of the Echinoderms of the British Isles*, Oxford University Press.

PHYLUM CHORDATA
44. Berrill, N. J. (1950) *The Tunicata with an account of the British species,* Ray Society, London.

OBSERVING, COLLECTING, PRESERVING
45. *Instructions for Collectors;* No. 9A, *Invertebrate Animals other than Insects* (1954); No. 4A, *Insects* (1963); No. 10, *Plants* (1965), British Museum (Natural History), London.

IDENTIFICATION, NOMENCLATURE
46. Kerrich, G. J., Meikle, R. D. and Tebble, N. (Edit.) (1967) *Bibliography of Key Works for the Identification of the British Fauna and Flora,* Systematics Association, British Museum (Natural History), London.
47. *Fiches d'Identification du Zooplankton,* Conseil Permanent International pour l'exploration de la mer 1949–1965. (A series of sheets providing keys and figures for identification of many planktonic animals).
48. Eales, N. B. (1961) *The Littoral Fauna of Great Britain,* Cambridge University Press.
49. Barrett, J. & Yonge, C. M. (1958) *Collins Pocket Guide to the Sea Shore,* Collins, London.
50. Cloudsley-Thompson, J. L. (1961) *Rhythmic Activity in Animal Physiology and Behaviour,* Academic Press.
51. Yonge, C. M. (1966) *The Sea Shore,* New Naturalist Series, No. 12, Collins, London.
52. Bullough, W. S. (1960) *Practical Invertebrate Anatomy,* Macmillan.
53. Buchsbaum, R. (1953) *Animals Without Backbones,* Penguin Books, 2 vols.
54. Savory, T. (1962) *Naming the Living World,* English University Press.
55. Rothschild, Lord. (1965) *A Classification of Living Animals,* Longmans.

INDEX

SOME OTHER TITLES IN THIS SERIES

■ **Arts**
Antique Furniture/Architecture/Art Nouveau for Collectors/Clocks and Watches/Glass for Collectors/Jewellery/Musical Instruments/Porcelain/Pottery/Silver for Collectors/Victoriana

■ **Domestic Animals and Pets**
Budgerigars/Cats/Dog Care/Dogs/Horses and Ponies/Pet Birds/Pets for Children/Tropical Freshwater Aquaria/Tropical Marine Aquaria

■ **Domestic Science**
Flower Arranging

■ **Gardening**
Chrysanthemums/Garden Flowers/Garden Shrubs/House Plants/Plants for Small Gardens/Roses

■ **General Information**
Aircraft/Arms and Armour/Coins and Medals/Espionage/Flags/Fortune Telling/Freshwater Fishing/Guns/Military Uniforms/Motor Boats and Boating/National Costumes of the world/Orders and Decorations/Rockets and Missiles/Sailing/Sailing Ships and Sailing Craft/Sea Fishing/Trains/Veteran and Vintage Cars/Warships

■ **History and Mythology**
Age of Shakespeare/Archaeology/Discovery of: Africa/The American West/Australia/Japan/North America/South America/Great Land Battles/Great Naval Battles/Myths and Legends of: Africa/Ancient Egypt/Ancient Greece/Ancient Rome/India/The South Seas/Witchcraft and Black Magic

■ **Natural History**
The Animal Kingdom/Animals of Australia and New Zealand/Animals of Southern Asia/Bird Behaviour/Birds of Prey/Butterflies/Evolution of Life/Fishes of the world/Fossil Man/A Guide to the Seashore/Life in the Sea/Mammals of the world/Monkeys and Apes/Natural History Collecting/The Plant Kingdom/Prehistoric Animals/Seabirds/Seashells/Snakes of the world/Trees of the world/Tropical Birds/Wild Cats

■ **Popular Science**
Astronomy/Atomic Energy/Chemistry/Computers at Work/The Earth/Electricity/Electronics/Exploring the Planets/Heredity/The Human Body/Mathematics/Microscopes and Microscopic Life/Physics/Psychology/Undersea Exploration/The Weather Guide